C000218238

MATHS
FOR PRACTICE & REVISION

3

ALGEBRA

PETER ROBSON

Newby Books

PO BOX 40, SCARBOROUGH
NORTH YORKSHIRE, YO12 5TW
TEL/FAX 01723 362713

A + ADDITION

Single letters of the same kind

a really means 1a , so

$$a + a = 2a$$

$$a + a + a = 3a$$

$$Y + Y + Y + Y + Y = 5Y$$

$$h + h + h + h + h + h + h = 7h$$, etc.

The number in front of a letter is a COEFFICIENT,

e.g. <u>2x</u> 2 is the coefficient of x

B Groups of letters of the same kind

e.g. $5A + 3A + A = 9A$

$$4c + 4c = 8c$$

$$W + 3W + W = 5W$$

REMEMBER Y really means 1Y, but it is always written Y
t really means 1t, but it is always written t, etc.

C Harder-looking Groups

When adding, the kinds of letters never change

e.g. $pq + pq + pq + pq = 4pq$

$$XYZ + XYZ = 2XYZ$$

$$DE + DE + DE + DE + DE + DE = 6DE$$

$$5ab + 6ab = 11ab$$

$$GP + 3GP + 4GP = 8GP$$

Note: pq can also be written qp
DE can also be written ED
XYZ can also be written XZY, YZX, YXZ, ZXY or ZYX, etc.

D Terms and Expressions

A TERM is a single group of figures

e.g. 25 is a term
y is a term
3cd is a term

An EXPRESSION is a collection of terms

e.g. $4a + 15$ is an expression
$pq + 3pq + 2pq$ is an expression

a

1) $y+y+y+y$
2) $K+K+K+K+K+K$
3) $h+h$
4) $A+A+A+A+A$
5) $m+m+m+m+m+$
   $m+m+m+m$
6) $E+E+E$
7) $p+p+p+p+p$
8) $N+N+N+N$
9) $T+T+T+T+T+T+T$
10) $c+c$
11) $q+q+q+q+q+q$
12) $B+B+B+B+B$
13) $x+x+x$
14) $J+J+J+J+J+J+J$
    $+J+J+J$
15) $v+v+v+v$

---

b

1) $2A + 3A$
2) $5G + G$
3) $4m + 4m$
4) $2R + 5R$
5) $p + 3p$
6) $6c + 5c$
7) $7w + 2w$
8) $6K + K + K$
9) $d + 3d + 4d$
10) $2 + 3 + 5$
11) $U + 4U + U$
12) $2z + z$
13) $5B + 7B$
14) $2a + 5a + 6a$
15) $0.7e + 1.3e + 0.4e$
16) $2y + 2y + 2y$
17) $2H + 3H + H + 2H$
18) $y + 5y + y + 2y$
19) $4G + 8G$
20) $5q + q + 4q$

---

c

1) $xy + xy + xy$
2) $ab + ab + ab + ab$
3) $uz + uz + uz + uz + uz$
4) $PQR + PQR + PQR$
5) $DF + DF$
6) $jk + jk + jk + jk$
7) $W+W+W+W+W+W$
8) $gh + gh + gh$
9) $st + st$
10) $BC+BC+BC+BC$
    $+BC+BC$
11) $6x + 5x + 4x$
12) $2ef + 2ef$
13) $mn + 2mn + 6mn$
14) $8F + 2F + F + 4F$
15) $ac + 6ac + ac$
16) $6yz + 2yz + 4yz$
17) $1.7RV + 3.9RV$
18) $A + A + A + 3A$
19) $j+j+j+j+j+j+j+j$
20) $bc + bc + bc + 4bc$

A + ADDITION (2)

Collecting LIKE TERMS

Letters of the same kind are called LIKE TERMS

*To add, collect together all the like terms

e.g. D + C + D + D + C

C + C = 2C

and D + D + D = 3D , so answer is 2C + 3D

(or 3D + 2C)

Some more examples

N + P + P + N + N + P + N = 4N + 3P

x + x + y + x + z + y = 3x + 2y + z

AB + PQ + PQ + AB + AB + AB = 4AB + 2PQ

B Groups of like terms

e.g. 3F + 4H + 7H + F + 2H = 4F + 13H

5b + 6a + 2b + 4c + 8a = 14a + 7b + 4c

C Ordinary numbers

Ordinary numbers are separate terms and must be added separately

e.g. Q + 6 + R + 5 + R = Q + 2R + 11

6j + 2j + 1 + j + 6 = 9j + 7

D Capital letters and small letters are different (unlike) terms and should be added separately

e.g. h and H are unlike terms, so

4H + 5h + 3h + 7H = 11H + 8h

E Simplify means 'work out to get the simplest possible answer'

e.g. Simplify 2a + 3b + 4a + 7b = **6a + 10b**

If there are **no like terms,** it is not possible to simplify.

e.g. 3P + 2R + 3Q cannot be simplified.

a

Add by collecting LIKE TERMS

1) a + a + p + a + p + p
2) s + h + s + s + h
3) b + j + b + b + j + b + b
4) V + c + c + c + V + c
5) W + V + W + V + W + W + V
6) F + F + G + G + F + G + G
7) t + M + M + t + t + t + t
8) AB + AB + D + AB + D
9) P + R + Q + P + Q + R + P + P + R
10) eg + mn + mn + mn + eg + eg

---

b

By collecting LIKE TERMS, find the answers to these
(Remember, 1A is always written A, 1y is always written y, etc.)

1) D + E + E + D + E
2) p + p + p + p + q + q + q
3) a + a + b + a + b + a + a
4) H + J + G + J + H + G
5) K + T + K + M + K + T
6) m + p + m + m + p + p
7) y + w + w + y + w + w
8) GH + J + GH + GH + GH
9) y + x + x + y + y + y
10) e + e + E + e + E + e + e

---

c

Simplify by collecting like terms

1) 2A + 3B + 4A + 4B
2) M + 3L + M + 3M
3) 4e + 2e + 8f + f
4) 3.5w + 2v + 4.7w + 3v
5) 2xy + 6A + 4A + 3xy
6) 6h + 5h + 4j + 2h
7) 2t + 5 + 4 + t
8) AB + 3AC + 4AB + AC
9) 5Y + 2.7 + 7Y + 1.8 + 3Y
10) 3pq + p + q + pq + 5q
11) 4a + 5b + 3c + 4b + 6c
12) 8 + xy + 4xy + 2 + xy
13) 5N + 4Q + 3P + 3Q + 7P + 2N
14) 6uv + 3 + uv + 2uv + 4 + 1
15) 12g + 14h + 23g + 15g + 6h

---

d

Simplify. If the question contains **no like terms**, write 'Not possible'

1) n + 2h + 3n + 5h + n
2) 4wx + 5wx + 3wx + 2wx
3) 3F + 5G + 2G + 2F
4) 6 + R + 2R + 2 + R
5) 4a + 6c + 5b + 3
6) q + 3t + t + 2t + q + 3q
7) 4L + 7M
8) 2J + 7 + 3K + 5 + J + 3K
9) 8p + 8p + 2p + 3q + q
10) 6m + 9n + 2k
11) 2f + 3f + 5 + 5g + 6f + g
12) 5a + 6a + 3a + 8a + 3a
13) 1 + PQ + 3 + PQ + PQ + 8
14) 18e + 19E + 17e + 7E
15) 4U + U + 6V + 3U + V

A + — ADDITION AND SUBTRACTION (Directed Numbers)

e.g. What is the value of 3 + 4 ?

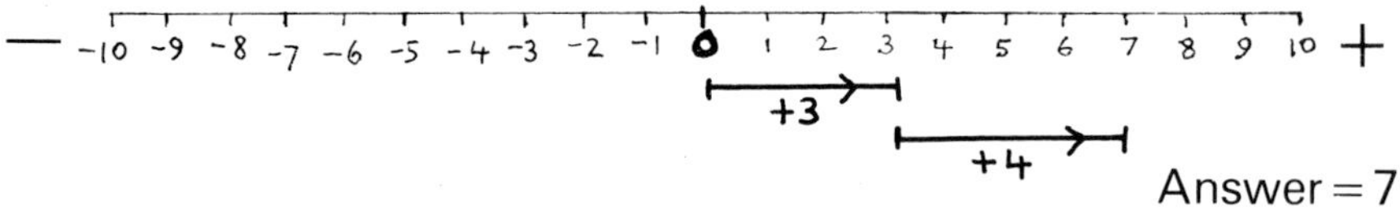

Answer = 7

e.g. What is the value of 5 — 8 ?

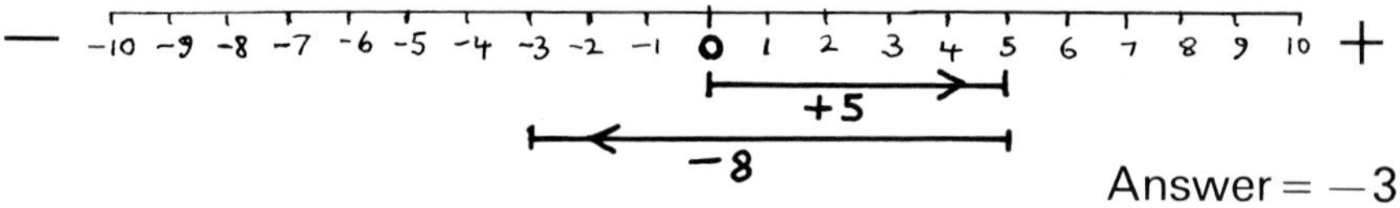

Answer = —3
(minus three)

e.g. What is the value of —4 + 10 ?

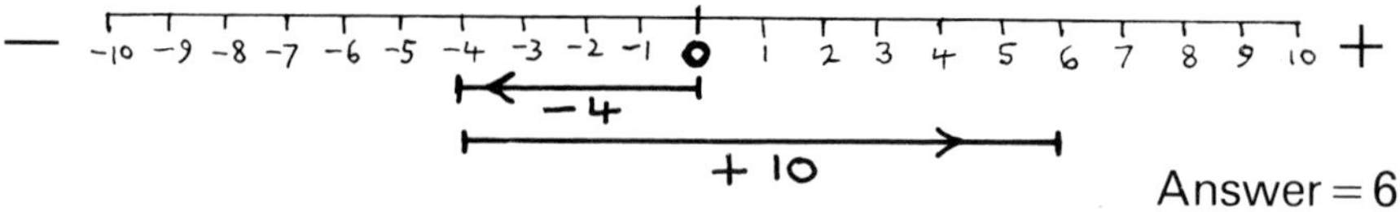

Answer = 6

B

e.g. What is the answer to —6—2 ?

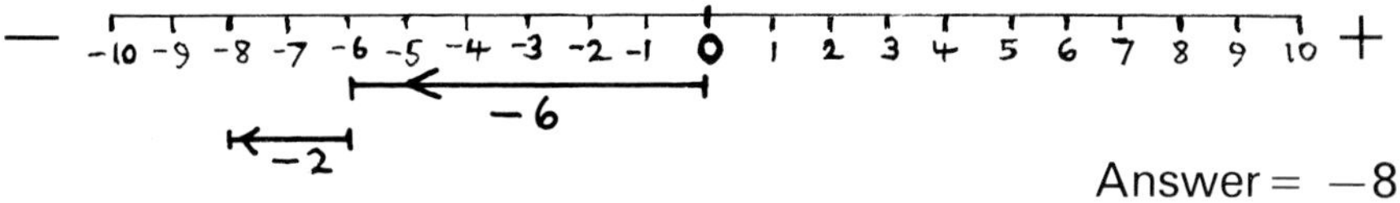

Answer = —8

e.g. —1 —7 —5 = —13
0—6 = —6 , etc.

C

e.g. What is the answer to 4 — 5 + 3 — 8 ?

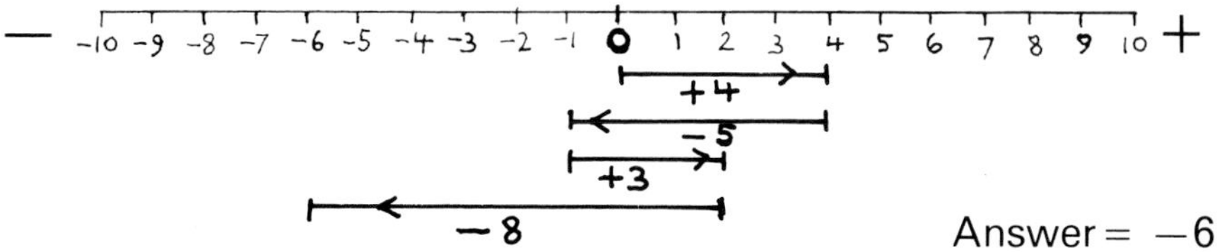

Answer = —6

e.g. —5 + 9 — 2 + 4 — 1 = 5
4 + 3 — 10 — 2 + 5 = 0, etc.

D

REMEMBER 5—3 = **2,** so 3—5 = **—2**
11—6 = **5,** so 6—11 = **—5**

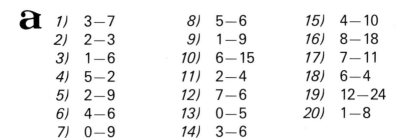

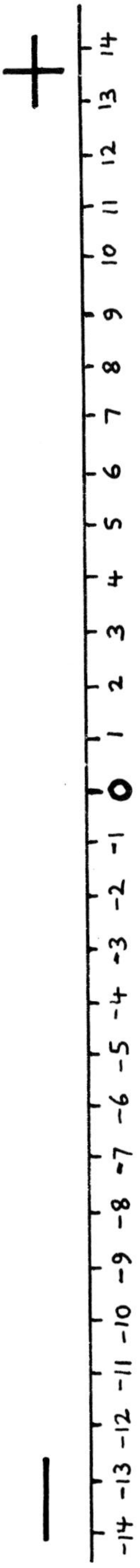

a

1) 3−7
2) 2−3
3) 1−6
4) 5−2
5) 2−9
6) 4−6
7) 0−9
8) 5−6
9) 1−9
10) 6−15
11) 2−4
12) 7−6
13) 0−5
14) 3−6
15) 4−10
16) 8−18
17) 7−11
18) 6−4
19) 12−24
20) 1−8

b

1) −1−1
2) −3−4
3) −5−7
4) −4−5
5) −3−1
6) −7−8
7) −4−3−2
8) −2−5
9) −6−2−3
10) −2−1−2
11) −9−3−5
12) 0−1−7
13) −3−3−3
14) −5−6−9
15) −2−1−4−3

c

1) 4−5+3
2) 1−3−4
3) −2+5+3
4) −4+5
5) 3+2−9
6) 5−5−7
7) 3−6+2
8) −2−3−4−5
9) 5−3+9
10) −4+6−2
11) −1−4+8
12) 7−11+4
13) 14−43
14) 1+5−12+2
15) 2−5+8−3

d

1) 0−3+1+4
2) 5−6−4
3) −2−7+3
4) 2−10+5−4
5) −1−3−8−1
6) 3−11−1 + 9
7) −3+1−3
8) 8−5−2
9) −4+3−6−1
10) 0+2−5
11) 5−9+6
12) 1−1−2−2
13) −13+4+1+2
14) 3−8+12
15) −2−7−1+5

A + — ADDITION AND SUBTRACTION (2)

Directed numbers (+ —, — —)

1) + — can be written —

e.g. $6 + -4 = 6 - 4 = 2$

$-5 + -7 = -5 - 7 = -12$

$8 + -2 + -9 = 8 - 2 - 9 = -3$

2) — — can be written +

e.g. $2 - -3 = 2 + 3 = 5$

$6 - -7 = 6 + 7 = 13$

$-2 - -4 - -1 = -2 + 4 + 1 = 3$

B Letters of the same kind

e.g. $z + z + z - z = 2z$

$-ab - ab + ab - ab + ab - ab = -2ab$

$8q - 2q = 6q$

$3UV + 5UV + 2UV - 3UV = 7UV$

$2r + 4r - 11r + r = -4r$

If the answer comes to 0, write 0 without the letter

e.g. $5kmn - 8kmn + 3kmn = 0$

C Collecting LIKE TERMS

* Collect each sort of term separately

e.g. $3A + 4B - A + 6A - 9B$

(1) Collect all A terms $3A - A + 6A = 8A$

(2) Collect all B terms $4B - 9B = -5B$

so final answer is $\underline{8A - 5B}$

If **part** of the answer comes to 0, leave it out

e.g. $4H - 6J + J + 5H + 5J =$ **9H**

If **all** the answer comes to 0, write 0

e.g. $5yz - 4wx + wx - 7yz + 3wx + 2yz =$ **0**

D REMEMBER

1) Ordinary numbers are different terms and must be collected separately.

e.g. $5st + 4a - 6 + 3st - 9 - 5a =$ **8st — a — 15**

2) Capital letters and small letters are different terms and must be collected separately.

a

1) $5 + \;-1$
2) $8 + \;-6$
3) $-2 + \;-5$
4) $7 - \;-2$
5) $4 + \;-4$
6) $1 - \;-12$
7) $-5 - \;-6$
8) $3 + \;-6$
9) $0 - \;-7$
10) $-9 + \;-9$
11) $-4 - \;-8$
12) $2 - \;-9$
13) $5 + \;-2$
14) $-11 - \;-3$
15) $7 + \;-2 + \;-2$
16) $-5 + \;-1 - \;-7$
17) $2 - \;-3 - \;-4$
18) $6 - \;-2 + \;-15$
19) $-1 + \;-8 - \;-4$
20) $-10 - \;-3 \;+9$

---

b

1) $c + c + c - c$
2) $T + T - T - T + T - T - T$
3) $k - k - k - k - k$
4) $w + w - w + w - w - w - w$
5) $DE + DE - DE + DE - DE$
6) $L + L - L + L + L + L$
7) $-JK - JK + JK - JK - JK$
8) $6m - 4m$
9) $3u - 7u$
10) $T - 8T$
11) $4x - 3x - 3x$
12) $a + 5a - 2a$
13) $2p - 6p + 4p$
14) $-3rs - rs - 3rs + 2rs$
15) $-3xyz - 4xyz + 9xyz$

---

c

Simplify by collecting LIKE TERMS

1) $3h + 2j + 7h - j$
2) $5C + 5D - 3D + 2C$
3) $4y - 3x + y - 2x$
4) $6b - 8b - 2a - a$
5) $4m + 2m + 3n + 6n$
6) $12P + 8p - 7P$
7) $3ac + 6tu + 5ac - 3tu$
8) $9K - 2 + 3K + 3 - 8K$
9) $4q - 6r + 2q - r + 2q$
10) $7EF + 5H + 2H - H$
11) $-3st + 5x + 3st + 4x - 9x$
12) $-3 - 2z - y - 8 + z$
13) $4g + 6h + 2h + 7g$
14) $N + 2P - P + 2N + 3P$
15) $-5jk + A - 6jk - 3A$

---

d

Simplify. If the question contains no like terms, write 'Not possible'.

1) $4y + 2x - 7y + x - 3y$
2) $3u - 5t - 7u + 3v + t - 2v$
3) $8ab + 12d - 10ab + 3d$
4) $-6W + 4W - 8Z + 2W + 8Z$
5) $-2mnp + 6mp - 6mnp + mp$
6) $5g + 3f + f + 8g - 11f$
7) $6m + 3n - 8 - 7mn$
8) $4d - d + 3a - 6a - 3d$
9) $-Q + R - 4Q - 8R$
10) $10J - 11KL + 3KL + 5M + 5J$
11) $3e + 7d - 14f + 8c$
12) $-3KLM + 4KLM - 7KLM + 12KLM$
13) $2xy - w - 9xy + 6w + 7xy - 5w$
14) $i + 3h - h + 3i + 5h - 5i$
15) $2A - 7B + 9A - 2B - A - 5B - 2A$

A +−ADDITION AND SUBTRACTION (3)

Powers (Indices)

In addition and subtraction, the small numbers at the top (powers, or index numbers) never change

e.g. $R^2 + R^2 + R^2 = 3R^2$

$m^3 + m^3 + m^3 + m^3 + m^3 = 5m^3$

$4W^2Y + 3W^2Y + 5W^2Y = 12W^2Y$

$7A^2 - A^2 = 6A^2$

$6c^4 - 8c^4 = -2c^4$

$-5P^5Q^4 - 3P^5Q^4 - 2P^5Q^4 = -10P^5Q^4$

$2mp^2 + 4mp^2 - 11mp^2 = -5mp^2$

$-7a^3b^2 + 8a^3b^2 - a^3b^2 = 0$

B Collecting LIKE TERMS

Collect each sort of term separately. Remember the powers (index numbers) never change.

e.g. $5N + 6x^2 + 2x^2 + 4N$

Collect all N terms $5N + 4N = 9N$

Collect all x^2 terms $6x^2 + 2x^2 = 8x^2$

so final answer is $\mathbf{9N + 8x^2}$

e.g. $4a^3 + 6a + 5a^2 + a + 7a^3 = \mathbf{11a^3 + 5a^2 + 7a}$

$-6p^2 - 8 + 4p - 4 + 5p^2 + p = \mathbf{5p - p^2 - 12}$

C

Terms must be EXACTLY alike, or they are not like terms

e.g. ab, a^2b, b, ab^2, a^2b^2, a are all different (unlike) terms and must be collected separately.

$4a^2b + 3ab^2 - 2a^2b^2 + 3ab^2 - 3a^2b = \mathbf{a^2b + 6ab^2 - 2a^2b^2}$

BUT ab and ba **ARE** LIKE TERMS

b^2a and ab^2 **ARE** LIKE TERMS

a^2b and ba^2 **ARE** LIKE TERMS

a

1) N^2+N^2
2) $a^3+a^3+a^3+a^3+a^3$
3) $M^2+M^2+M^2$
4) $x^4+x^4+x^4+x^4+x^4$
5) c^5+c^5
6) $qr^2+qr^2+qr^2+qr^2$
7) $B^6+B^6+B^6+B^6+B^6+B^6+B^6$
8) $y^2+y^2+y^2+y^2$
9) $gh^2+gh^2+gh^2$
10) $c^3d^2+c^3d^2+c^3d^2+c^3d^2$
11) AB^2+AB^2
12) $v+v+v+v+v+v+v$
13) $J^4+J^4+J^4+J^4+J^4+J^4$
14) $v^2w+v^2w+v^2w$
15) $h^2j^3+h^2j^3$

---

b

1) $7p^3+4p^3$
2) $5A^2+A^2$
3) $12m^2n-4m^2n$
4) $6st^3-6st^3$
5) $9G+7G$
6) wy^2-4wy^2
7) $4b^4c+10b^4c$
8) $8k^7-k^7$
9) $3abc^2-2abc^2$
10) $-4F^4-8F^4$
11) $2q^2r^2+7q^2r^2$
12) $6U^2+5U^2$
13) $3j^5-8j^5$
14) $-2y^3z-11y^3z$
15) $4TU^2-9TU^2+3TU^2$
16) $3d^4+d^4-6d^4$
17) $5m^2n^3-8m^2n^3+3m^2n^3$
18) $V^2-6V^2-6V^2$
19) $-7pt^3+8pt^3-5pt^3$
20) $-2x^2y+3x^2y$

---

c

1) $4y+5y+3y^2+4y^2$
2) $3E^2+7E+E^2+2E+E^2$
3) $3p^3+2p^2+4p^2+6p^3$
4) $2B^2+6B-3B+5B^2-B$
5) $5Q^2R^2+3QR-Q^2R^2-2QR$
6) $m^2+4n^2-5m^2-7n^2$
7) $6-4K^4+7K^4-13$
8) $-2c^5-3c^6-5c^5-4c^6$
9) $3LM-5L-4LM+6L$
10) $4pqr+3pq^2-5pq^2+pqr$
11) $bc-2b^2c-bc+6b^2c$
12) $2z^8+7z+4z-12z+z^8$
13) $6g^4h^3-10g^4h^3+g^4h^3$
14) $4vw^2-3vw+6v^2w+8vw$
15) $8J^5-3J^5-5J^2-2J^2$

---

d

Simplify. If the question contains no like terms, write 'Not possible'.

1) $4tu^2+5t^2u+3t^2u+7tu^2$
2) $D^2+6D^3+D^2-9D^3$
3) $2y^2z^3-4y^3z^2+7y^3z^2+3y^2z^3$
4) $4jk+6jk^2-3jk^2-jk^2$
5) $3mn+4m^2n+mn^2+5n$
6) $8e-4e^2-6e+e-e^2$
7) $-5KT^2-12K^2T^2+6KT^2+5K^2T^2$
8) $6q^2-4q^4-5q+9q^3$
9) $-7c^2d+2cd+4c^2d-5cd$
10) $PR^4+3PR^4-4R^4-4PR^4+R^4$
11) $-w^2-7w-7w+4w^2+w$
12) $3ab^3+4ab-6ab^2+4a^3b$
13) $9x+9x^3+9x^2+9$
14) $2h+pq-h-10pq-h$
15) $4C^3-2C^2+6C+5C^2+C^3$

A ×MULTIPLICATION

Numbers and Letters

e.g. $2 \times A = 2A$

$4 \times x = 4x$

$W \times 7 = 7W$

$2 \times c \times 3 = 6c$

Note that the number (the coefficient) is always written first, and the letter afterwards

e.g. **8a** and not a8

B Letters × Themselves

e.g. $y \times y = y^2$ (y SQUARED)

$M \times M \times M \times M \times M = M^5$ (M TO THE POWER 5)

$z \times z \times z = z^3$ (z CUBED)

$b \times b \times b \times b \times b \times b = b^6$ (b TO THE POWER 6)

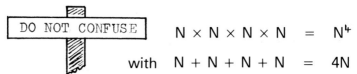

$N \times N \times N \times N = N^4$

with $N + N + N + N = 4N$

If in doubt, think of ordinary numbers

e.g. $5 \times 5 \times 5 = 125$

which is very different from $5 + 5 + 5 = 15$

C Numbers × Letters × Themselves

e.g. $2N \times 3N$

*1) Multiply numbers $2 \times 3 = 6$

*2) Then multiply letters $N \times N = N^2$

so $2N \times 3N = \mathbf{6N^2}$

D Mixed Letters

$a \times b = ab$

$r \times s = rs$

$xy \times z = xyz$

$C \times B \times A = ABC$

$m \times p \times n = mnp$

Write letters in ALPHABETICAL ORDER

e.g. $r \times p \times q = pqr$

a

1) $3 \times a$
2) $M \times 5$
3) $4 \times h$
4) $2 \times y$
5) $7 \times q$
6) $2 \times 4 \times F$
7) $5 \times k$
8) $c \times 2$
9) $12 \times t$
10) $A \times 3 \times 5$
11) $N \times 4$
12) $6 \times m$
13) $R \times 3$
14) $5 \times x \times 2$
15) $9 \times H$
16) $3 \times 2 \times p$
17) $C \times 3 \times 3$
18) $Y \times 4$
19) $4 \times g \times 5$
20) $7 \times 2 \times T$

---

b

1) $a \times a \times a$
2) $N \times N$
3) $e \times e \times e \times e$
4) $p \times p \times p$
5) $m \times m$
6) $V \times V \times V \times V \times V$
7) $f \times f \times f \times f$
8) $R \times R \times R \times R \times R \times R$
9) $x \times x$
10) $j \times j \times j \times j \times j$
11) $t \times t \times t \times t \times t \times t$
12) $W \times W \times W \times W$
13) $y \times y \times y \times y \times y \times y \times y \times y$
14) $D \times D \times D \times D \times D$
15) $r \times r \times r \times r \times r \times r \times r$

---

c

1) $2A \times 4A$
2) $6H \times H$
3) $a \times 3a$
4) $3G \times 7G$
5) $2p \times p$
6) $5y \times 3y$
7) $2D \times 2D$
8) $m \times 8m$
9) $4Q \times 3Q$
10) $5x \times x$
11) $y \times y \times 4y$
12) $2B \times 8B$
13) $5 \times L \times L$
14) $2u \times 2u \times 2u$
15) $6n \times 7n$
16) $T \times T \times T \times T \times 5$
17) $4 \times 4w \times w$
18) $K \times 2K \times 3K$
19) $2c \times 3c$
20) $Z \times 4Z \times 3Z \times Z$

---

d

Write answers in ALPHABETICAL ORDER

1) $c \times a$
2) $s \times t$
3) $w \times x$
4) $P \times Q$
5) $H \times F$
6) $w \times a$
7) $d \times e \times f$
8) $T \times V \times W$
9) $b \times a \times c$
10) $k \times p \times m$
11) $pq \times r$
12) $H \times FG$
13) $a \times c \times b \times d$
14) $M \times N \times J$
15) $yz \times xw$
16) $B \times g \times k$
17) $q \times mn$
18) $RW \times PT$
19) $u \times w \times v$
20) $jk \times m \times p$

---

e

1) $c \times c \times c \times c \times c$
2) $M + M + M$
3) $3h \times 4h$
4) $9j + j + 2j$
5) $3z - 7z + 5z$
6) $d \times 2d \times 4d$
7) $7b \times 5b$
8) $q \times q \times q \times q$
9) $8E - 5E - E$
10) $8n \times 5n \times n$
11) $R + R + R + R + R + R + R$
12) $7 \times k \times 2$
13) $m \times 2m \times 3$
14) $2A + 3A - 6A$
15) $y \times 3 \times y \times 3y$
16) $4f + 5f$
17) $5i \times 4i$
18) $m \times k \times h \times 2$
19) $T - 5T - 3T$
20) $x \times 5x \times 3$

A ×MULTIPLICATION (2)

Numbers × Mixed letters e.g. $5T \times 4U$

*1) Multiply coefficients (numbers) $5 \times 4 = 20$
*2) Multiply letters $T \times U = TU$

so $5T \times 4U =$ **20TU**

Some more examples

$$m \times 4k = 4km$$
$$3G \times 2H = 6GH$$
$$2y \times 2z \times 2w = 8wyz$$
$$\tfrac{1}{2}a \times 12b = 6ab$$
$$4t \times 2rs = 8rst$$

B Powers × Powers

*When multiplying, **ADD** the powers

e.g. $a^3 \times a^2 = a^5$

$$y^7 \times y^2 = y^9$$
$$c^4 \times c^4 \times c^4 = c^{12}$$

REMEMBER x really means x^1

so $x \times x^2 \times x = x^4$

$H^2 \times H^5 \times H = H^8$, etc.

C Mixed Letters, Powers and Numbers

e.g. $3A^2B \times 6AB^4$

*1) Multiply coefficients $3 \times 6 = 18$
*2) Multiply each letter separately $A^2 \times A = A^3$
$B \times B^4 = B^5$

so answer is $\mathbf{18A^3B^5}$

Some more examples

$$4x^2 \times 3xy = 12x^3y$$
$$\tfrac{1}{3}KL^2 \times 6K^3L^2 = 2K^4L^4$$

D Squares and Cubes of Terms

e.g. $(2a)^2$ means $2a \times 2a$, so answer is $4a^2$
$(3xy)^2$ means $3xy \times 3xy$, so answer is $9x^2y^2$
$(2M)^3$ means $2M \times 2M \times 2M$, so answer is $8M^3$
$(x^2y^4)^3$ means $x^2y^4 \times x^2y^4 \times x^2y^4$, so answer is x^6y^{12}

Other powers work just the same way

e.g. $(2c)^5 = 2c \times 2c \times 2c \times 2c \times 2c = \mathbf{32c^5}$

a

1) $d \times 2e$
2) $4A \times 3B$
3) $5x \times y$
4) $2j \times 2k$
5) $3h \times 3m$
6) $6P \times 4Q$
7) $3c \times d$
8) $4x \times 2y \times 2z$
9) $3s \times 2t$
10) $2N \times 5P$
11) $4m \times 2n$
12) $7 \times a \times 3b$
13) $6g \times 2f$
14) $2R \times 9S$
15) $u \times 7v$
16) $\frac{1}{2}a \times 6c$
17) $3k \times 3 \times 3h$
18) $5 \times p \times 3r$
19) $10Y \times \frac{1}{2}Z$
20) $T \times 6U$

---

b

1) $y^2 \times y^3$
2) $d \times d^2$
3) $W^5 \times W^7$
4) $b^3 \times b$
5) $Z \times Z \times Z^2$
6) $e^3 \times e^3$
7) $Q \times Q^3 \times Q$
8) $h^5 \times h^6$
9) $T \times T^2 \times T^3$
10) $M^2 \times M^2$
11) $p^5 \times p^3$
12) $A^2 \times A \times A^2$
13) $K^4 \times K^5$
14) $u^2 \times u^2 \times u^2 \times u^2$
15) $n \times n^6$
16) $X^3 \times X^2$
17) $G^4 \times G^4 \times G^3$
18) $q^2 \times q^2 \times q^3$
19) $j^6 \times j \times j^2$
20) $N \times N \times N^4 \times N$

---

c

1) $4L^2 \times 2L^2$
2) $5C \times 5C^2$
3) $2W^4 \times W^3$
4) $8i^3 \times 3i^2$
5) $3Y^6 \times 5Y$
6) $3b^4 \times 2b^4$
7) $7E^3 \times E$
8) $6J^4 \times 2J^3$
9) $2x \times 5x^4$
10) $3v^2 \times 2v \times 2v$
11) $8M^3 \times 2M^3$
12) $2 \times 2q^5 \times 2q^3$
13) $3D^4 \times 5D$
14) $t^2 \times 3t^{10}$
15) $8H^4 \times \frac{1}{2}H^2$
16) $3F \times 4F^2 \times 5F^2$
17) $6a^2 \times 6a^2$
18) $4r^5 \times r^4 \times r^3$
19) $2p^7 \times 4 \times 3p$
20) $7k^2 \times 3k^{11}$

---

d

1) $2x^2 \times 3y$
2) $4AB \times A^2B^3$
3) $5jk^2 \times 2k$
4) $3q^2r^2 \times 5q^2r^2$
5) $TW \times 6W^4$
6) $7c^2 \times 5cd$
7) $2LM \times 2LM$
8) $ax^2 \times a^2x^5$
9) $6D \times D^5E$
10) $9g^3h \times 2h^2$
11) Multiply $2P$ by $3PQ$
12) Find the product of $3W^3$ and $4V^2W$
13) Multiply b^3c by b^2c^4
14) Find the product of $3f^2g$ and $2fg^2$
15) Find the product of $12M$ and $\frac{1}{2}LM$

---

e

1) $(4B)^2$
2) $(2y)^3$
3) $(mn)^2$
4) $(q^2)^2$
5) $(3H)^2$
6) $(C^2)^3$
7) $(3a)^3$
8) $(2V)^4$
9) $(PQR)^2$
10) $(3f)^3$
11) $(5L)^3$
12) $(\frac{1}{2}H)^2$
13) $(2t)^5$
14) $(J^2K)^9$
15) $(4d)^3$

÷DIVISION

Division by a number

*Write as a FRACTION and cancel numbers if possible.

e.g. $2a \div 2$ | $12x \div 3$ | $30y \div 5$ | $6m \div 12$

$$\frac{{}^1\cancel{2}a}{\cancel{2}_1}$$ $$\frac{{}^4\cancel{12}x}{\cancel{3}_1}$$ $$\frac{{}^6\cancel{30}y}{\cancel{5}_1}$$ $$\frac{{}^1\cancel{6}m}{\cancel{12}_2}$$

a   4x   6y $\dfrac{m}{2}$

IMPORTANT. If an answer containing letters looks IMPROPER
(top heavy), LEAVE IT AS IT IS. Do not try to make it into a
mixed number.

e.g. $8h \div 5$ $14M \div 8$

$$\frac{8h}{5}$$ $$\frac{{}^7\cancel{14}M}{\cancel{8}_4}$$

$$\frac{7M}{4}$$

B Division by a letter

*Write as a fraction and cancel letters if possible.

e.g. $4p \div p$ | $cd \div d$ | $W \div T$ | $N \div N$

$$\frac{4\cancel{p}^1}{\cancel{p}_1}$$ $$\frac{c\cancel{d}^1}{\cancel{d}_1}$$ $$\frac{W}{T}$$ $$\frac{\cancel{N}^1}{\cancel{N}_1}$$

4   c   1

If in doubt, write out in full. Then cancel.

e.g. $A^2 \div A$ | $k^2m^2 \div k$ | $6p^3q \div p$ | $y^5 \div y$

$$\frac{{}^1\cancel{A} \times A}{\cancel{A}_1}$$ $$\frac{\cancel{k} \times k \times m \times m}{\cancel{k}_1}$$ $$\frac{6 \times \cancel{p}^1 \times p \times p \times q}{\cancel{p}_1}$$ $$\frac{\cancel{y}^1 \times y \times y \times y \times y}{\cancel{y}_1}$$

A km^2 $6p^2q$ y^4

C Division by numbers and letters

e.g. $18A \div 3A$ | $24x^3 \div 8x$ | $10HJ \div 2J$ | $4R \div 8RT$

$$\frac{{}^6\cancel{18}\cancel{A}^1}{{}_1\cancel{3}\cancel{A}_1}$$ $$\frac{{}^3\cancel{24}\cancel{x}^3 x^2}{{}_1\cancel{8}\cancel{x}_1}$$ $$\frac{{}^5\cancel{10}H\cancel{J}^1}{{}_1\cancel{2}\cancel{J}_1}$$ $$\frac{{}^1\cancel{4}\cancel{R}^1}{{}_2\cancel{8}\cancel{R}T}$$

6          $3x^2$ 5H $\dfrac{1}{2T}$

a

1) $9c \div 3$
2) $14H \div 2$
3) $6y \div 6$
4) $12k \div 4$
5) $20A \div 5$
6) $8e \div 1$
7) $24W \div 4$
8) $12t \div 3$
9) $21N \div 7$
10) $16V \div 8$
11) $18L \div 2$
12) $a \div 8$
13) $4d \div 4$
14) $E \div 5$
15) $30p \div 6$
16) $15f \div 3$
17) $7U \div 1$
18) $9M \div 9$
19) $6j \div 2$
20) $x \div 10$

---

b

1) $2x \div 3$
2) $B \div 2$
3) $4m \div 5$
4) $6Z \div 4$
5) $2A \div 10$
6) $6Q \div 7$
7) $8c \div 6$
8) $3t \div 6$
9) $16w \div 4$
10) $R \div 3$
11) $3g \div 8$
12) $28D \div 7$
13) $4K \div 12$
14) $8s \div 10$
15) $3u \div 6$
16) $18P \div 2$
17) $N \div 5$
18) $24J \div 4$
19) $\frac{1}{2}a \div 3$
20) $2y \div 8$

---

c

1) $6n \div n$
2) $3Y \div Y$
3) $7f \div f$
4) $AB \div B$
5) $mp \div m$
6) $JKL \div K$
7) $4t \div t$
8) $x \div x$
9) $wx \div w$
10) $P \div R$
11) $6yz \div z$
12) $3np \div m$
13) $2BC \div A$
14) $4cd \div d$
15) $5e \div e$
16) $9q \div q$
17) $g \div f$
18) $12tu \div t$
19) $b \div b$
20) $mn \div n$

---

d

1) $G^2 \div G$
2) $W^3 \div W$
3) $a^2b^2 \div b$
4) $T^4 \div T$
5) $x^2y \div y$
6) $J^2K \div J$
7) $p^2q^2 \div q$
8) $gh \div g$
9) $C^2D^3 \div D$
10) $4M^2 \div M$
11) $3r^3 \div r$
12) $8n^3p \div n$
13) $u^4w^5 \div u$
14) $2v^4 \div v$
15) $7A^2 \div A$

---

e

1) Divide $10rv$ by $2r$
2) Divide $9MN$ by $3M$
3) Divide $4PT$ by $12T$
4) Divide 1 by $4q$
5) Divide $6hn$ by $6h$
6) Divide $15ak$ by $5k$
7) Divide $8jm$ by $4jm$
8) Divide $30de$ by $3d$
9) Divide $14pq$ by $21q$
10) Divide $6f^2$ by $3f$
11) Divide $16v^3$ by $2v$
12) Divide $12b$ by $4ab$
13) Divide $4R^2$ by $2R$
14) Divide $18u^2z$ by $2z$
15) Divide $20k$ by $5jk$

A ÷DIVISION

Powers ÷ Powers

*When dividing, SUBTRACT the powers

e.g. $W^7 \div W^4 = W^3$

$b^{10} \div b^2 = b^8$

$Y^5 \div Y^4 = Y$

$3^6 \div 3^2 = 3^4$

$m^3 \div m^3 = m^0 = 1$

If in doubt, write out in full. Then cancel.

e.g. $x^6 \div x^4 = \dfrac{x \times x \times x \times x \times x \times x}{x \times x \times x \times x} = \dfrac{x^2}{1} = x^2$

B Mixed letters, powers and numbers

*Write as a fraction. Then cancel numbers and letters if possible. REMEMBER to **SUBTRACT** powers.

e.g. $24F^7 \div 3F^2$

$\dfrac{{}^{8}\,24F^7\;F^5}{{}_{1}\,3F^2\;{}_{1}}$

$8F^5$

$18PR^3 \div 12P^2R$

$\dfrac{{}^{3}\,18PR^3\;R^2}{{}_{2}\,12P^2_{\;P}R}$

$\dfrac{3R^2}{2P}$

C Division with multiplication

*Multiply first.
Then cancel.

e.g. $\dfrac{8g^2h^2 \times 2hk}{6ghk}$

$\dfrac{{}^{8}\,16g^2h^3k\;{}^{1}}{{}_{3}\,6ghk\;{}_{1}}$

$\dfrac{8gh^2}{3}$

D Division with addition and subtraction

*1) Write denominator under EACH NUMERATOR

*2) Divide each term separately

e.g. $\dfrac{6b^2c - 10abc}{2bc}$

$\dfrac{{}^{3}\,6b^2c}{2bc} - \dfrac{{}^{5}\,10abc}{{}_{1}\,2bc}$

$3b - 5a$

a

1) $C^9 \div C^2$
2) $n^3 \div n$
3) $L^6 \div L^3$
4) $x^{10} \div x^4$
5) $Z^5 \div Z^5$
6) $F^{11} \div F^3$
7) $q^5 \div q$
8) $i^7 \div i^6$
9) $A^2 \div A^5$
10) $t^8 \div t^2$
11) $7^5 \div 7^2$
12) $V^4 \div V^4$
13) $m^2 \div m^7$
14) $d^9 \div d^5$
15) $H \div H^3$

---

b

1) $20k^6 \div 4k^3$
2) $8G^8 \div 2G^6$
3) $7b^4 \div b^3$
4) $9e^{12} \div 3e^5$
5) $2W^6 \div W^2$
6) $D^5 \div 4D^3$
7) $16r^8 \div 12r^3$
8) $3M^4 \div 3M^4$
9) $6h^5 \div 10h^4$
10) $12a^2 \div 6a^6$
11) $18C \div 3C^2$
12) $6tu^2 \div 2u$
13) $22k^2n \div 2kn^2$
14) $5A^3J^4 \div 15AJ$
15) $wxy \div 8w^2x$
16) $7PQ \div 3P^2R$
17) $2s^2t \div 6s^4t^2$
18) $10y^3z^2 \div 14yz$
19) $12ad^2 \div 2ad$
20) $35f^3g^3 \div 5f^3g^3$

---

c

1) $\dfrac{4x \times 5y}{2y}$

2) $\dfrac{2A \times 12B}{3ABC}$

3) $\dfrac{3pq \times 4q^3}{6p^2q}$

4) $\dfrac{8mn \times 3m^2}{24m^3n}$

5) $\dfrac{10Y^2 \times 2YZ}{5Y^3Z^3}$

6) $\dfrac{5tu \times 3wx}{30uw}$

7) $\dfrac{18G^2J}{3J^2 \times 2GJ^2}$

8) $\dfrac{9c^2d^3 \times 8c^3d^3}{4d^2 \times 3c^4}$

9) $\dfrac{2R^2 \times 2P^3R}{20P^2R^2}$

10) $\dfrac{2JK \times 4JK}{8K^3 \times 3J^3}$

---

d

1) $\dfrac{8xy + 12x^2}{4x}$

2) $\dfrac{25E^2F + 10E}{5E}$

3) $\dfrac{R - 5R^3}{R}$

4) $\dfrac{6a^3b + 4a^2b^2}{2ab}$

5) $\dfrac{g^4h^3 - 3gh^5}{gh^2}$

6) $\dfrac{15p^2rt - 6p^3t^3}{3p^2t}$

7) $\dfrac{30K^3L^2 + 18KL}{3KL}$

8) $\dfrac{12w^3z^3 - 6w^2z^4}{6w^2z^2}$

9) $\dfrac{4m^2 - 12mn}{2m}$

10) $\dfrac{3C^5D^4 + C^4D^5}{C^3D^3}$

A × ÷ MULTIPLICATION AND DIVISION WITH − SIGN

A + quantity × or ÷ a + quantity = a + quantity

e.g. $5 \times 6 = 30$

$12 \div 3 = 4$

A + quantity × or ÷ a − quantity = a − quantity

e.g. $5 \times -6 = -30$

$12 \div -3 = -4$

A − quantity × or ÷ a + quantity = a − quantity

$-5 \times 6 = -30$

$-12 \div 3 = -4$

A − QUANTITY × OR ÷ A − QUANTITY = A + QUANTITY

$-5 \times -6 = 30$

$-12 \div -3 = 4$

REMEMBER. The answer to a MULTIPLICATION or DIVISION is always the same **SIZE,** whatever the original signs.

e.g. 8×4 always gives 32 as the answer,

but $8 \times -4 = -32$

$-8 \times 4 = -32$

$-8 \times -4 = 32$

Some more examples

$9 \times -2 = -18$	$-20 \div 4 = -5$
$-3 \times -5 = 15$	$8.4 \div -7 = -1.2$
$-2 \times 0.8 = -1.6$	$-42 \div -6 = 7$
$\frac{1}{2} \times -5 = -2\frac{1}{2}$	$-25 \div 4 = -6\frac{1}{4}$
$-7 \times -4 = 28$	$-5\frac{1}{4} \div -7 = \frac{3}{4}$

B

e.g.

$$\underbrace{2 \times -4}_{-8} \times -5$$

$$-8 \times -5 = 40$$

$$\underbrace{-3 \times -3}_{9} \times -3$$

$$9 \times -3 = -27$$

$$\underbrace{-4 \times 2}_{-8} \times -3 \div -6$$

$$\underbrace{-8 \times -3}_{24} \div -6$$

$$24 \div -6 = -4$$

a

1) 2×-7
2) -3×1
3) -6×-3
4) 4×-2
5) 5×3
6) -8×9
7) -1×-1
8) 14×-2
9) -5×-6
10) -11×5
11) -4×6
12) -9×-5
13) 3×-2
14) -43×-11
15) -7×7

---

b

1) $-15 \div 3$
2) $-8 \div -4$
3) $-7 \div 1$
4) $24 \div -6$
5) $-45 \div 5$
6) $-22 \div -2$
7) $10 \div 2$
8) $63 \div -9$
9) $-40 \div -5$
10) $12 \div -12$
11) $-36 \div -6$
12) $-126 \div 7$
13) $95 \div -5$
14) $-42 \div -21$
15) $-1 \div -1$

---

c

1) $-5.4 \div 2$
2) $1\frac{1}{2} \times -1\frac{1}{2}$
3) -2.6×-4
4) $3.5 \div -7$
5) $-5 \div -3\frac{1}{3}$
6) 0.6×-0.2
7) $-\frac{5}{6} \times -\frac{3}{5}$
8) 1.7×-3
9) $5\frac{2}{5} \div -\frac{9}{10}$
10) $-0.8 \div -2$
11) $-\frac{1}{3} \div 4$
12) $-6.8 \div -0.4$
13) $-2\frac{1}{2} \times 3\frac{1}{7}$
14) 36×-2.5
15) $-0.72 \div 24$

---

d

1) $2 \times -2 \times 3$
2) $-5 \times 4 \times 6$
3) $-3 \times -1 \times 1$
4) $8 \times 2 \times -2$
5) $-4 \times -2 \times -3$
6) $6 \times -5 \div 2$
7) $-42 \div 2 \div -3$
8) $1 \times -1 \times 13$
9) $-3 \times -7 \times -5$
10) $10 \times 10 \times -10$
11) $-9 \times 3 \times -2$
12) $-1 \times -2 \times -12$
13) $4 \times -7 \div 2$
14) $-20 \times -6 \div 15$
15) 43×-43

---

e

1) $5 \times -2 \times -4$
2) -21×-13
3) $6 \times 6 \times -6$
4) $-4 \times \frac{1}{2} \times -3$
5) $8 \div -1 \div 1$
6) $-56 \div -4 \div 2$
7) $-8 \times -3 \times 0$
8) $-5 \times 3 \times 2 \div 30$
9) $-24 \div -4 \times -2\frac{1}{2}$
10) $(-9)^2$
11) $-2 \times 3 \times -4 \times 2$
12) $(-4)^3$
13) $-\frac{1}{4} \times -\frac{2}{3} \times \frac{3}{5}$
14) $5 \times -\frac{1}{4} \div \frac{1}{2}$
15) $(-2)^4$

A ×÷MULTIPLICATION AND DIVISION WITH — SIGN (2)

A + quantity × or ÷ a + quantity = a + quantity

e.g. $2N \times 3P = 6NP$

$15ab \div 5b = 3a$

A + quantity × or ÷ a − quantity = a − quantity

e.g. $2N \times -3P = -6NP$

$15ab \div -5b = -3a$

A − quantity × or ÷ a + quantity = a − quantity

e.g. $-2N \times 3P = -6NP$

$-15ab \div 5b = -3a$

A − QUANTITY × OR ÷ A − QUANTITY = A + QUANTITY

e.g. $-2N \times -3P = 6NP$

$-15ab \div -5b = 3a$

Some more examples

1) $-2v^4 \times 3v^3$

$-6v^7$

2) $-20DE \div -4E$

$\dfrac{-20DE}{-4E}$

$5D$

3) $-7x^2y^2 \times -6x^3y^4$

$42x^5y^6$

4) Find the square of $-4NR^3$

$-4NR^3 \times -4NR^3$

$16N^2R^6$

5) $\dfrac{-2uw^2 \times -4u^2w^2}{-10u^3w}$

$\dfrac{8u^3w^4}{-10u^3w}$

$-\dfrac{4w^3}{5}$

a

1) $4 \times -w$
2) $-5 \times e$
3) $-2 \times -H$
4) $7 \times -AB$
5) $-10 \times xy$
6) $2 \times -3 \times M$
7) $6 \times -tu$
8) $18x \div 2$
9) $-12k \div 4$
10) $-5P \div 2$
11) $15st \div -3$
12) $-8ij \div 4$
13) $-4BC \div -2B$
14) $7xy \div -1$
15) $-2c \times -6d$
16) $18vw \div -3w$
17) $5pq \times 0$
18) $-27c \div -9c$
19) $-3w \div -6$
20) $-4y \times -4w$

---

b

1) $-7K \times -7K$
2) $-2d \times 3d$
3) $-3p \times pq$
4) $-ae \times -5e$
5) $-2yz \times -3yz$
6) $-6p^2 \div 3p$
7) $4h^3 \times -4k^2$
8) $-2B^4 \times -5B$
9) $-m^2n^3 \div mn$
10) $18st \div -3st^2$
11) $4B \times -C \times 2A$
12) $3n \times -n \times -6$
13) $-2R \times 2 \times -S$
14) $9eh \times -2h \times -e$
15) $-3wx \times 4wx \times -2w$
16) $-4HL \times 2HL \times -3HL$
17) $-5q^3r \times -3r^2 \times -q$
18) $\frac{1}{2}g \times -4fg \times -3f^2$
19) $4W^2Y \div -12W^4Y^4$
20) $-10d^3 \times 4d^3 \times \frac{1}{5}d^2$

---

c

1) Multiply $-8J$ by $4JK$
2) Find the square of $-3p^2w^3$
3) Divide $-24C^3D$ by $6CD$
4) Multiply the product of $-6mr^2$ and $3m^3r^3$ by $-2m^2r$
5) Divide $-15N$ by $-18N^2$
6) Calculate the product of $4u^4$ and $-7u^7$
7) Multiply $16y$ by $-3z$ and divide the result by -12
8) Find the product of $-5h^3i^2$ and $5h^3i^2$
9) Calculate the square of $-9PQ^2$
10) Divide by $-8A^2B$ the product of $-3B^2$ and $-6A$

---

d

1) $8y \div 8y$
2) $4w + 3w - 9w$
3) $R \times 5R \times 3R$
4) $-3d \div 4d$
5) $(7v)^2$
6) $6.2A - 1.9A$
7) $\frac{1}{2}t \times 8r \times \frac{1}{4}s$
8) $-4p^2 - 4p^2$
9) $-4p^2 \times 4p^2$
10) $-4p^2 \div 4p^2$
11) $-4p^2 + 4p^2$
12) $H + H + H - H + H$
13) $t^2 \times t^3 \times t^2$
14) $4z^3 + 5z^3 - z^3$
15) $6g + 5h - g - 6h$
16) $5qr \times 2r \times 2q$
17) $3wx^2 \div 15w^2x$
18) $4jk - 8k - jk + 2k$
19) $6abc \times -2abd$
20) $5u^2 + 2u - 4u^2 - 2u$

A ( ) BRACKETS

Multiplying out

*Each term in a bracket must be multiplied by the number or letter directly in front (on the left) of the bracket.

e.g.

$$5(A+B) = 5A + 5B$$
$$2(H-7) = 2H - 14$$
$$3(2n+p) = 6n + 3p$$
$$4(2E - F + 4G) = 8E - 4F + 16G$$
$$y(w-2) = wy - 2y$$
$$J(J+K) = J^2 + JK$$

B Signs

<u>REMEMBER</u> A MINUS TIMES A PLUS GIVES A **MINUS**
A MINUS TIMES A MINUS GIVES A **PLUS**

e.g.

$$-6(m + 2w) = -6m - 12w$$
$$-3(3q - r) = -9q \mathbf{+} 3r$$
$$-4d(-d + 2e) = 4d^2 - 8de$$
$$-A(2B + C - 5D) = -2AB - AC \mathbf{+} 5AD$$

A MINUS SIGN in front of a bracket means 'Multiply by −1'

e.g. $-(8N - 7) = \mathbf{-}8N \mathbf{+} 7$

C

Simplifying with brackets e.g. $4x - 3(x + 2y)$

*1) Multiply out brackets **FIRST.** Numbers and letters not directly in front of the bracket do not affect the bracket. $4x \quad -3x \quad -6y$

*2) Collect LIKE TERMS $x - 6y$

Some more examples

1)	2)	3)
$5n + 2n(3 + n)$	$4(2E - F) - 3F$	$2(3M-5) - (2M-7)$
$5n + 6n + 2n^2$	$8E - 4F - 3F$	$6M - 10 - 2M + 7$
$11n + 2n^2$	$8E - 7F$	$4M - 3$

a

Multiply out

1) $3(n+m)$
2) $2(b+c)$
3) $4(E+2)$
4) $a(x+y)$
5) $7(p-k)$
6) $2(h-5)$
7) $c(b-a)$
8) $6(3y-x)$
9) $3(2n-3t)$
10) $h(p-q)$
11) $M(M+4)$
12) $d(3+d^2)$
13) $J(5-J)$
14) $q(2p-5q)$
15) $8(2+2A)$

b

Multiply out

1) $-2(1+3D)$
2) $-4(x+w)$
3) $-(B-3)$
4) $5(3+w)$
5) $-e(e+8)$
6) $n(r-3s)$
7) $-9(-E-A)$
8) $-(m+q)$
9) $y(3y-4x)$
10) $-2(7h-\frac{1}{2}k)$
11) $-(W-4T+3U)$
12) $-c(6+2c)$
13) $5(3j-5)$
14) $\frac{1}{2}(4+2z)$
15) $-8(-2a-3b-c)$

c

Multiply out

1) $4y(2-x)$
2) $2g(h+5)$
3) $-3f(d+1)$
4) $6N(2-2M)$
5) $-2w(2v-3)$
6) $5(-e-4b)$
7) $4x(2x+6)$
8) $-3H(2J-3H)$
9) $a(a^2+5)$
10) $D(2D-D^2)$
11) $Z^2(Z-8)$
12) $-4p(-3q-r)$
13) $2t(t+t^2)$
14) $-4y(3-2y)$
15) $b^2(-b^2+5)$

d

Multiply out and simplify

1) $7t+5(t-7)$
2) $M+2(M+4)$
3) $d+4(2+d)$
4) $3a-2(a+6)$
5) $4(y-1)+6$
6) $5C+3(3+C)$
7) $12v-v(7+v)$
8) $2(5-3n)-3n$
9) $3a(2c+a)+2ac$
10) $8-3(3-2x)$
11) $3Q(3P-Q)+5Q^2$
12) $5-\frac{1}{2}(4U+6)$
13) $-f(5+j)+11f$
14) $4+2(2Z+7)$
15) $y+2y(3y+4)$

e

Multiply out and simplify

1) $2(3a+4)+3(a+2)$
2) $4(5+3Y)-2(2Y-3)$
3) $5(2m+1)-(1+4m)$
4) $3(2-4e)+6(2e-1)$
5) $W(W+4)-5(3-W)$
6) $-3(j-2k)-5(k-3j)$
7) $4(4a+3b)+2(c-5d)$
8) $\frac{1}{3}(12x-3)-(5+3x)$
9) $2M(7+2N)-N(3M+8)$
10) $c(4c-15)+7(2c+c^2)$

A ( ) BRACKETS (2)

Addition and Subtraction

e.g. Find the sum of $a+2b$, $3a-b$ and $b-a$

*1) Place brackets round each quantity — $(a+2b),\ (3a-b),\ (b-a)$

*2) Add and simplify — $(a+2b) + (3a-b) + (b-a)$

$$a+2b + 3a-b + b-a$$

$$3a + 2b$$

---

e.g. Subtract $5n - 3p$ from $n + 2p$

*1) Place brackets round each quantity — $(5n-3p),\ (n+2p)$

*2) Subtract and simplify — $(n + 2p) - (5n - 3p)$

READ THE QUESTION CAREFULLY and make sure you have set out the correct way round.

$$n + 2p - 5n + 3p$$

$$5p \quad -4n$$

REMEMBER, a MINUS sign in front of a bracket really means -1.

B

e.g. What must be added to 6 to make 10?

*Subtract (BE CAREFUL WHICH WAY ROUND!)

$$10 - 6$$

$$4$$

---

e.g. To what must $2x + y - 4$ be added to give $4y - 3x$?

*1) Place brackets round each quantity — $(2x + y - 4),\ (4y - 3x)$

*2) Subtract and simplify — $(4y - 3x) - (2x + y - 4)$

$$4y - 3x - 2x - y + 4$$

$$3y - 5x + 4$$

---

e.g. What must be subtracted from P to give $2Q - 3P$?

$$P - (2Q - 3P)$$

$$P - 2Q + 3P$$

$$4P - 2Q$$

a

1) Add together $c + d$, $2c - d$ and $3c + 4d$.
2) Calculate the sum of $5t - u$ and $6u - 4t$.
3) Subtract $L - 2M$ from $3L + M$
4) From $4w$ subtract $V + w$.
5) What is the sum of $3a - 4b$, $6b - 4a$ and $a - 2b$?
6) Find the total of $8p + 3$, $2 - p$ and -7.
7) Subtract $6EF + 4HJ$ from $7EF + HJ$
8) Add $7z$, $x - y$, $9y + 5x$ and $z - 6x$
9) From $4p - 3q - r$ subtract $3p - q + r$.
10) Take $6 + 7k$ away from 8.

---

b

1) Subtract $3f + 7g - 7$ from $8g + 3f$.
2) To the sum of $2T - R$ and $3Q - 4T$, add $Q + 2R - 3T$.
3) Subtract $3 + 5h$ from the sum of $9 + h$ and $3h - 7$.
4) Calculate the sum of $ab - 3b^2$ and $5b^2 + 3ab$.
5) Subtract $3K - L$ from 0
6) What must be added to 328 to give 506?
7) From the sum of $4d + 2c$ and $d - 5c$, subtract $2d + 3c$.
8) To what must 23 be added to give 17?
9) Take $5mn + 7$ from the sum of $6 - 2mn$ and $7mn - 1$.
10) What amount, added to -11, makes a total of 37?

---

c

1) What must be added to $y + 2z$ to give $5y + 9z$?
2) To what must A be added to make 50?
3) What must be subtracted from $6j + k$ to give $3k - j$?
4) What be must added to $bc - 4$ to give $4bc$?
5) Calculate the amount that must be added to $J + 4H$ to make $2J + H$
6) To what must $5m + 3$ be added to give $3 + 6m$?
7) What must be taken away from N to leave 13?
8) From what must $3D + 4$ be subtracted to give $7D + 6$?
9) What must be added to $3x^2 - xy + 1$ to give $4x^2 - 2xy - 5$?
10) From the sum of $3q + p - 8$ and $2r - 7q$, subtract the sum of $4p - 4q$ and $1 + r - 3p$.

A ( ) BRACKETS (3)

Factorisation

This is really the opposite of 'multiplying out', starting with the answer and working back to the brackets.

e.g. Factorise as far as possible $18p - 30q$

*1) Find the highest number which will divide into all the terms (the H.C.F. of the terms)

$18p$ will divide by 6
$-30q$ will divide by 6

*2) Write this number in front of brackets $6(\quad)$

*3) Divide each term by the number

$18p \div 6 = 3p$
$-30q \div 6 = -5q$

so answer is $6(3p - 5q)$

Sometimes a letter (or letters, or numbers AND letters) will divide into all the terms

e.g.

$$5a + 3ab = a(5 + 3b)$$
$$2PQR + QRS = QR(2P + S)$$
$$8mn - 12np = 4n(2m - 3p)$$
$$3y - 6xy = 3y(1 - 2x)$$

REMEMBER. When dividing terms containing powers (indices), the powers must be SUBTRACTED

e.g.

$$c^3 - 4c = c(c^2 - 4)$$
$$8PQ^4 + 9P^2Q = PQ(8Q^3 + 9P)$$
$$12f^2gh - 21fg^3 = 3fg(4fh - 7g^2)$$
$$15a^2bc - 10a^5b^3 = 5a^2b(3c - 2a^3b^2)$$

a

Copy and complete

1) $2a + 2b = 2(\quad + \quad)$
2) $6x + 9y = 3(\quad + \quad)$
3) $12w + 6 = 6(\quad + \quad)$
4) $20N - 8P = 4(\quad - \quad)$
5) $6m + 10k = 2(\quad + \quad)$
6) $28h - 7g = 7(\quad - \quad)$
7) $3uv - 5u = u(\quad - \quad)$
8) $12m + 16p - 4q$
   $= 4(\quad + \quad - \quad)$
9) $4bc + 9cd = c(\quad + \quad)$
10) $6xy + 10x = 2x(\quad + \quad)$

---

b

Factorise as far as possible

1) $5H - 5J$
2) $8w + 14x$
3) $9 - 6B$
4) $8ef - 12g$
5) $18N + 15M$
6) $18j - 9k$
7) $km + kn$
8) $24T - 18U$
9) $HJ + 3H$
10) $xy - wx$
11) $6d - 2f + 4g$
12) $5m - 2mn$
13) $6LP + 11JL$
14) $16R - 8Q$
15) $At + 9A$

---

c

Factorise as fully as possible

1) $12t - 3u + 9w$
2) $10AB + 7BC$
3) $6p - 3pq$
4) $8FH - 10EF$
5) $9hjk - 8jkm$
6) $25y + 10xy$
7) $12m - 8n + 20$
8) $9tvw - 33t$
9) $5AC + 2CE - 9BC$
10) $4xyz - 6yz$
11) $2N^2 + N^2P^2$
12) $3uv^2 + 5v^3$
13) $12C^2D - 9CD^2$
14) $3qtu + 4p^2qt$
15) $2AB^2C + 7B^2$
16) $12FG + 8GH^2$
17) $8k + 2m - 12n$
18) $18y^2z^3 + 12xz^2$
19) $Q^3R - Q^2R^2$
20) $9g^3k^2 + 3gk$

---

d

Simplify each of these expressions, and then FACTORISE each answer as fully as possible.

1) $3m + 4n + 2m + n$
2) $c + d - 9d + 3c$
3) $2(p - q) + 4(q + p)$
4) $8K - 4(3J - 4K)$
5) $3(5y + 3) - 4$
6) $5GH - 3G^2 - 3GH + 4G^2$
7) $9(A - 2B) - 3(B + 4)$
8) $4(2TU - U^2) + 6U^2$
9) $c - 2a + 5c - 12b + 8a$
10) $5(R - Q) - 7(Q + R)$

A ALGEBRA FRACTIONS

Addition and subtraction

*1) Find lowest common denominator

*2) Work out new numerators (tops)

*3) Add or subtract numerators

e.g.

$$\frac{D}{2} + \frac{2D}{3}$$

$$\frac{}{6} + \frac{}{6}$$

$$\frac{3D}{6} + \frac{4D}{6}$$

$$\frac{7D}{6}$$

IMPORTANT. If an answer containing letters looks IMPROPER (top-heavy), LEAVE IT AS IT IS. Do not try to make it into a mixed number.

e.g.

$$\frac{4y}{5} + \frac{3y}{4} - \frac{7y}{10} \qquad \frac{16y}{20} + \frac{15y}{20} - \frac{14y}{20} \qquad \frac{17y}{20}$$

$$\frac{21c}{8} - \frac{3c}{4} \qquad \frac{21c}{8} - \frac{6c}{8} \qquad \frac{15c}{8}$$

$$\frac{3F}{2} - \frac{5G}{4} \qquad \frac{6F}{4} - \frac{5G}{4} \qquad \frac{6F - 5G}{4}$$

$$\frac{4}{y} + \frac{1}{3y} \qquad \frac{12}{3y} + \frac{1}{3y} \qquad \frac{13}{3y}$$

B +— with larger numerators

*1) Write brackets round each numerator

*2) Find lowest common denominator, and work out new numerators.

*3) Add or subtract numerators (MIND SIGNS!)

e.g.

$$\frac{2a+3}{5} - \frac{a-4}{3}$$

$$\frac{(2a+3)}{5} - \frac{(a-4)}{3}$$

$$\frac{(6a+9)}{15} - \frac{(5a-20)}{15}$$

$$\frac{6a+9-5a+20}{15}$$

$$\frac{a+29}{15}$$

C ×÷ Multiplication and division

*1) Invert (turn upside down) any term after a ÷ sign

*2) Cancel if possible

*3) Multiply (Top × top, bottom × bottom)

e.g.

$$\frac{2Y}{5Z} \times \frac{3}{2W} \div \frac{Y}{10}$$

$$\frac{2Y}{5Z} \times \frac{3}{2W} \times \frac{10}{Y}$$

$$\frac{{}^{1}\cancel{2}\cancel{Y}^{1}}{{}_{1}\cancel{5}Z} \times \frac{3}{{}_{1}\cancel{2}W} \times \frac{\cancel{10}^{2}}{\cancel{Y}_{1}}$$

$$\frac{6}{WZ}$$

NEVER ADD OR SUBTRACT BOTTOMS

a

1) $\frac{K}{3} + \frac{K}{4}$
2) $\frac{2p}{5} + \frac{3p}{10}$
3) $\frac{7a}{3} - \frac{3a}{2}$
4) $\frac{G}{9} + \frac{G}{6}$
5) $\frac{5m}{2} - \frac{11m}{8}$
6) $\frac{2c}{3} + \frac{4c}{5}$
7) $\frac{5R}{6} - \frac{3R}{4}$
8) $\frac{y}{4} + \frac{9y}{10}$
9) $\frac{5E}{3} - \frac{13E}{9}$
10) $4h - \frac{13h}{4}$
11) $\frac{J}{8} + \frac{J}{4} + \frac{J}{2}$
12) $\frac{t}{2} + \frac{t}{6} - \frac{t}{3}$
13) $\frac{3N}{2} + \frac{2N}{5} + \frac{N}{4}$
14) $\frac{4w}{3} - \frac{w}{2} - \frac{5w}{6}$
15) $\frac{4Q}{3} - \frac{5Q}{6} + \frac{3Q}{8}$

b

1) $\frac{5J}{6} - \frac{K}{2}$
2) $\frac{4pq}{5} + \frac{3pq}{4}$
3) $\frac{a}{2} + \frac{5n}{7}$
4) $\frac{7h}{4} - \frac{2}{3}$
5) $\frac{3w}{2} - \frac{7x}{6} - \frac{4w}{3}$
6) $\frac{1}{c} - \frac{1}{2c}$
7) $\frac{1}{2p} + \frac{2}{3p}$
8) $\frac{3}{4A} + \frac{2}{A}$
9) $\frac{5}{4h} - \frac{1}{2h}$
10) $\frac{3}{x} + \frac{6}{y}$
11) Find the sum of $\frac{5R}{8}$ and $\frac{Q}{12}$
12) Subtract $\frac{3M}{5}$ from $\frac{5M}{3}$
13) From the sum of $\frac{H}{3}$ and $\frac{7H}{6}$, subtract $\frac{5H}{9}$
14) Subtract $\frac{6d}{7}$ from $\frac{2c}{5}$
15) Find the sum of $\frac{4}{5}$, $\frac{3a}{2}$ and $\frac{a}{10}$

c

1) $\frac{a+2}{3} + \frac{2a+1}{2}$
2) $\frac{Y+4}{2} - \frac{Y}{5}$
3) $\frac{3-c}{6} + \frac{c-2}{4}$
4) $\frac{4k+3}{4} - \frac{1+k}{8}$
5) $\frac{2N-5}{4} - \frac{N-4}{3}$
6) $\frac{2B}{3} + \frac{A-B}{5}$
7) $\frac{5-f}{4} - \frac{1-3f}{2}$
8) $\frac{V}{9} - \frac{2-V}{3}$
9) $\frac{q+3r}{4} + \frac{5q-2r}{10}$
10) $\frac{2J-3H}{5} - \frac{H+J}{6}$

d

1) $\frac{t}{2} \times \frac{u}{5}$
2) $\frac{3}{y} \times \frac{w}{6}$
3) $\frac{B}{10} \times \frac{15A}{2}$
4) $\frac{y}{6} \times \frac{y}{4}$
5) $\frac{F}{3} \div \frac{F}{12}$
6) $\frac{12}{M} \times \frac{N}{8}$
7) $\frac{ab}{j} \times \frac{c}{hk}$
8) $\frac{7R}{15} \div \frac{T}{6}$
9) $\frac{3}{4R} \div \frac{3P}{4}$
10) $\frac{1}{4D} \times \frac{6D}{5}$
11) $\frac{6x}{y} \times \frac{5y}{8} \times \frac{x}{5}$
12) $\frac{15u}{tw} \times \frac{w}{u} \div \frac{9w}{4t}$
13) $\frac{1}{2c} \times \frac{1}{2a} \times \frac{1}{2b}$
14) $\frac{12q}{7p} \div \frac{3p}{2} \div \frac{pq}{14n}$
15) $\frac{3H}{9F} \times \frac{8G}{H} \div \frac{5G}{F}$

A PERIMETER, AREA AND VOLUME

PERIMETER of a figure is the distance all the way round the figure

e.g. Find the perimeter of a rectangle (3x + 1) centimetres long and 2x centimetres wide.

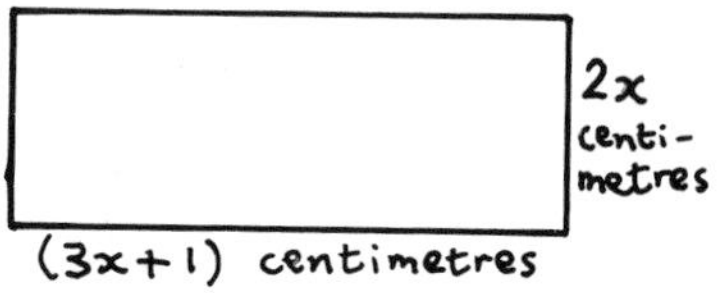

*1) Add together the lengths of all the sides
$(3x + 1) + 2x + (3x + 1) + 2x$

*2) Make sure answer is simplified as far as possible **(10x + 2) centimetres**

B AREA

AREA of a rectangle = Length × Width

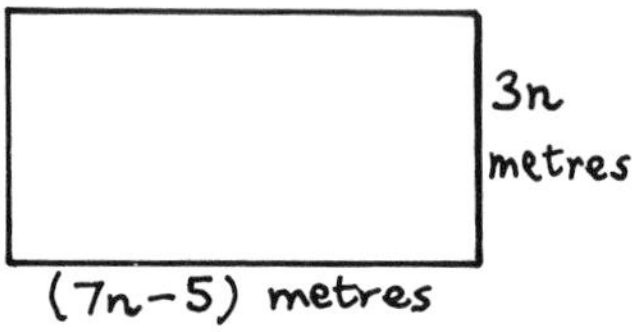

e.g. Calculate the area of a rectangular field (7n − 5) metres long and 3n metres wide.

$(7n - 5) \times 3n$

($21n^2 - 15n$) square metres

C VOLUME

VOLUME of a cuboid = Length × Width × Height

e.g. Find the volume of a cuboid 4w centimetres long, 3w centimetres wide and w centimetres high.

Volume = $4w \times 3w \times w$

$12w^3$ cubic centimetres

D

In algebra, it is safer to write out units IN FULL to avoid any confusion

e.g. **$5y^2$ square centimetres** is clearer than **$5y^2cm^2$**

$8a^3$ cubic metres is clearer than **$8a^3m^3$**

a Find (i) the perimeter, and (ii) the area, of each of these rectangles.

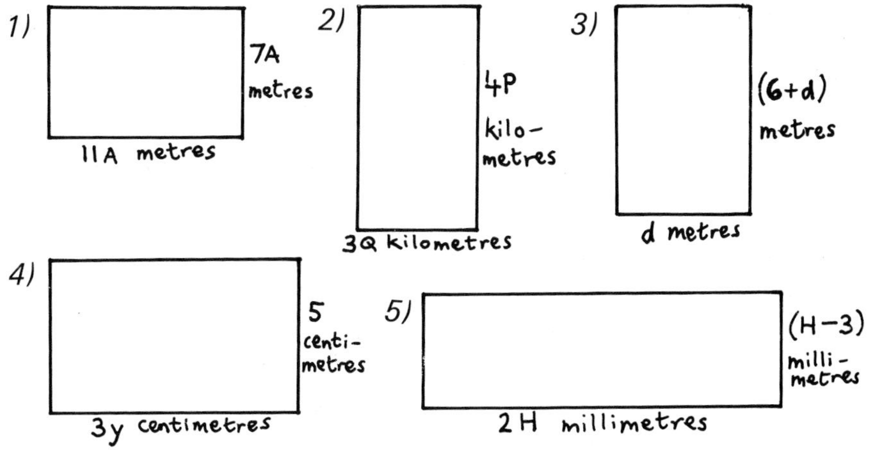

b All the shapes in these questions are rectangles.

1) The length of a playing field is 9L metres and its width is 6L metres. What is its area?
2) Find the area of an airport runway 7k metres long and 5j metres wide.
3) What is the area of a photograph which has length $5T/6$ centimetres and width $3T/4$ centimetres?
4) The length of a carpet was 3 times its width. If its width was 4x metres, what was its area?
5) A map shows an area of land $(3b + 2)$ kilometres long and 2b kilometres wide. What area of land is shown on the map?

c All the objects in these questions are cuboids.

1) Find the volume of a tank p centimetres long, q centimetres wide, r centimetres high.
2) Calculate the volume of a box of length 4y centimetres, width 3y centimetres and height y centimetres.
3) A block of wood has length $(N + 20)$ millimetres, width N millimetres and height N millimetres. What is its volume?
4) What is the volume of a container 5k centimetres long, 5k centimetres wide and 5k centimetres high?
5) A boating pool was 35a metres long, 20a metres wide and 2a metres deep. If it were filled right to the top with water, what volume would it hold?

A SUBSTITUTION

SUBSTITUTION means replacing, or substituting, a letter with a number, so that the answer (the VALUE) comes out as a number.

e.g. If A = 2, B = 3, C = 1, find the values of

A + B	B + C	C − B	B + C − A
2 + 3	3 + 1	1 − 3	3 + 1 − 2
5	4	−2	2

B

e.g. If x = 4, y = 2, z = 0, find the values of

5x	3z	xy	6y	3xy
5 × 4	3 × 0	4 × 2	6 × 2	3 × 4 × 2
20	0	8	12	24

REMEMBER. Anything multiplied by 0 equals **0**

C

e.g. If h = 1, j = 4, k = 6, find the values of

$\frac{k}{h}$	$\frac{j}{k}$	$\frac{3j}{k}$	$\frac{kj}{3h}$
	$\frac{4}{6}$	$\frac{3 \times 4}{6}$	$\frac{6 \times 4}{3}$
$\frac{6}{1}$	$\frac{\cancel{4}^{2}}{\cancel{6}_{3}}$	$\frac{{}^{1}\cancel{3} \times \cancel{4}^{2}}{\cancel{6}\,\cancel{3}_{1}}$	$\frac{{}^{2}\cancel{6} \times 4}{\cancel{3}_{1}}$
6	$\frac{2}{3}$	2	8

D

e.g. If L = 2, M = 3, N = 1, find the values of

L^2	N^3	$2M^2$	$3L^2M$
L × L	N × N × N	2 × M × M	3 × L × L × M
2 × 2	1 × 1 × 1	2 × 3 × 3	3 × 2 × 2 × 3
4	1	18	36

VERY IMPORTANT

$5N^2$ means 5 × N × N (not 5N × 5N)

$2L^3$ means 2 × L × L × L (not 2L × 2L × 2L)

a

If p = 4, q = 3, r = 2, t = 1, find the values of

1) $p + q$
2) $p + r$
3) $p - t$
4) $q - r$
5) $p + q + r$
6) $t - p$
7) $q + r$
8) $p + q - r$
9) $p + t + q$
10) $t - q + r$
11) $q - p$
12) $q - p + r$
13) $t + q + q$
14) $p - q - t$
15) $p + q + p$
16) $t - p - q$
17) $p + q + r + t$
18) $q - t - p$
19) $r - q + t - p$
20) $q + p + r - t$

b

REMEMBER. Anything multiplied by 0 equals **0.**

If K = 6, L = 3, M = 0, N = 2, find the values of

1) 2L
2) 4K
3) 3M
4) KL
5) 5N
6) 6K
7) LM
8) 3KN
9) 4L
10) −4LN
11) 12N
12) KM
13) 5NL
14) 2KLMN
15) NK
16) ½K
17) KLN
18) 7N
19) ⅓L
20) ¼M

c

If a = 4, b = 6, c = 3, d = 2, find the values of

1) $\frac{a}{d}$
2) $\frac{b}{c}$
3) $\frac{b}{d}$
4) $\frac{c}{b}$
5) $\frac{d}{b}$
6) $\frac{3a}{d}$
7) $\frac{2b}{c}$
8) $\frac{bd}{a}$
9) $\frac{4b}{ad}$
10) $\frac{ba}{c}$
11) $\frac{bcd}{9}$
12) $\frac{5d}{a}$
13) $\frac{abc}{4d}$
14) $\frac{3cd}{a}$
15) $\frac{ca}{db}$

d

If r = 2, t = 3, w = 1, find the values of

1) r^3
2) t^2
3) $3w^2$
4) $2r^2$
5) t^4
6) $4t^2$
7) w^3
8) r^5
9) wt
10) r^2t^2
11) tr^3
12) $3r^4$
13) wr^2
14) t^2w
15) $2t^3$
16) $\frac{6r^2}{t}$
17) $4rtw$
18) $\frac{5r^3}{4}$
19) $\frac{9r^3}{2t^2}$
20) $3tr^2$

A SUBSTITUTION (2)

Two or more terms

e.g. If $f=3$, $g=6$, $h=2$, find the value of $5h^2 - fg$

*1) Write BRACKETS round each term but **not** round the signs $(5h^2) - (fg)$

*2) Work out each bracket separately $(5 \times 2 \times 2) - (3 \times 6)$

$(20) - (18)$

*3) Remove brackets and finish off $20 - 18$

2

ALWAYS WORK **DOWN** THE PAGE (not across)

B

Minus Signs (Negative quantities)

A **MINUS** TIMES A **PLUS** GIVES A **MINUS**
A **MINUS** TIMES A **MINUS** GIVES A **PLUS**

e.g. If $y=4$, $z=-2$, find the value of $3z - 2y$

$(3z) - (2y)$

$(3 \times -2) - (2 \times 4)$

$(-6) - (8)$

−14

e.g. (2) If $n = -3$, $p = 4$, find the value of $\frac{3p}{2} - 5n$

$\left(\frac{3p}{2}\right) - (5n)$

$\left(\frac{3 \times 4}{2}\right) - (5 \times -3)$

$(6) - (-15)$

$6 + 15$

21

Always work out each bracket first, before doing the signs.

VERY IMPORTANT

1) $4y^3$ means $4 \times y \times y \times y$ (not $4y \times 4y \times 4y$)
$7A^2$ means $7 \times A \times A$ (not $7A \times 7A$)

2) $(-3)^2$ means $-3 \times -3 = +9$

a

If $E = -1$, $F = 4$, $G = 2$, $H = 8$, find the values of these expressions. Remember to write each term in a bracket and then work out the value of each bracket before doing the signs.

1) $2G + 3F$
2) $6G - H$
3) $2H - 4F$
4) $H^2 + F^2$
5) $3G^2 + 5F$
6) $\frac{H}{G} + 3E$
7) $2F^2 - 5G$
8) $3H - 7F$
9) $F - \frac{E}{G}$
10) $4E^2 + F$
11) $\frac{H^2}{F^3} - GH$
12) $E + 4G^3$
13) $2G - 3H$
14) $F^2 - 6G^2$
15) $\frac{H}{G} + \frac{E}{F}$

---

b

If $a = 4$, $f = -1$, $m = 3$, $t = -2$, find the values of

1) $a + t$
2) $f + m$
3) $m - t$
4) $t + f$
5) $4a + m$
6) $2m - 4f$
7) $a + 2t$
8) $2a - 3m$
9) $3t - f$
10) $4t + 2m$
11) $am + t$
12) $at - fm$
13) $3fa + 4m$
14) $5m - ft$
15) $2f - 4t$

---

c

If $p = 5$, $q = 2$, $r = -3$, $s = 1$, find the values of

1) $5q - p$
2) $s - 4q$
3) $p + 2r$
4) $6s - 3r$
5) $q^2 + p^2$
6) $3r + r^2$
7) $2rs - p$
8) $p - r^2$
9) $qp - 2r$
10) $4pr + 8q^2$
11) $7p + 5qr$
12) $4q^2 - 2p^2$
13) $pqrs$
14) $\frac{3q}{2} - 3r$
15) $\frac{6r}{q} + p$

---

d

If $b = -3$, $c = 2$, $d = 3$, $e = -4$, evaluate

1) $c + d + e$
2) $2d + 3e + c$
3) $3b - 2d + 7c$
4) $b^2 + c^2 + d^2$
5) $4c + d + 3b$
6) $5d + 2c - 2e$
7) $2c^2 - 4d + b$
8) $4d^2 + 5e + 7b$
9) $2e - 3b + 6d$
10) $bc + de + be$
11) $3d^2 + b - 5e$
12) $\frac{de}{2} - bc^2$
13) $\frac{8d}{c} + 5b + \frac{e^2}{2}$
14) $3c^2d - 2e^2 + 2b$
15) $\frac{e}{c} - \frac{4b}{d} - \frac{d}{e}$

A SUBSTITUTION (3)

Fractions

e.g. If $L = 3$, $M = \frac{2}{3}$, $N = 4$, what is the value of $6MN - 9LM^2$

*1) Write brackets round each term but **not** round the signs

$$(6MN) - (9LM^2)$$

*2) Work out each bracket separately

$$(6 \times \tfrac{2}{3} \times 4) - (9 \times 3 \times \tfrac{2}{3} \times \tfrac{2}{3})$$

If whole numbers and fractions are mixed together, put whole numbers over 1 to make sure cancelling is correct.

$$(\tfrac{6}{1} \times \tfrac{2}{3} \times \tfrac{4}{1}) - (\tfrac{9}{1} \times \tfrac{3}{1} \times \tfrac{2}{3} \times \tfrac{2}{3})$$

*3) Finish off

$$(16) - (12)$$

$$4$$

Sometimes the final stage must also be worked out as a fraction.

e.g. If $x = 1\frac{1}{5}$, $y = 4$, $z = -\frac{1}{6}$, find the value of $12xz^2 - 2yz$

$$(12xz^2) - (2yz)$$

$$(\tfrac{12}{1} \times \tfrac{6}{5} \times -\tfrac{1}{6} \times -\tfrac{1}{6}) - (\tfrac{2}{1} \times \tfrac{4}{1} \times -\tfrac{1}{6})$$

$$(\tfrac{2}{5}) - (-\tfrac{4}{3})$$

$$\tfrac{2}{5} + \tfrac{4}{3}$$

$$\tfrac{26}{15}$$

$$1\tfrac{11}{15}$$

REMEMBER. 'Squared' means 'times itself'

e.g. If $a = \frac{3}{4}$, $b = 2$, find the values of

$8a^2$	$(b - a)^2$
$8 \times a \times a$	$(b - a) \times (b - a)$
$\frac{8}{1} \times \frac{3}{4} \times \frac{3}{4}$	$(2 - \frac{3}{4}) \times (2 - \frac{3}{4})$
$\frac{9}{2}$	$1\frac{1}{4} \times 1\frac{1}{4}$
$4\frac{1}{2}$	$\frac{25}{16}$
	$1\frac{9}{16}$

a

If $a = \frac{3}{4}$, $b = 2$, $c = 1$, find the values of

1) $a + b$
2) $c + 2a$
3) abc
4) a^2
5) $3b^2c$
6) $4a - 3c$
7) $a - \frac{c}{b}$
8) $c^2 + 2ab$
9) $8a^2 - b^2$
10) $a - c$

b

If $n = 3$, $p = \frac{1}{3}$, $q = \frac{2}{3}$, $r = 4$, find the values of

1) $q + p$
2) nq
3) $3q - 2r$
4) $q - p$
5) $6q - 2p$
6) $q^2 - p$
7) $3pr + 9q$
8) $\frac{p}{q} + \frac{n}{r}$
9) $\frac{1}{2}pn^2 - 3q^2$
10) $\frac{2r}{n} - npqr$

c

If $w = \frac{1}{3}$, $x = 0$, $y = 6$, $z = 1\frac{1}{2}$, find the values of

1) $2wy + 3z - y^2x$
2) $yz - y^2 + 12w$
3) $\frac{1}{2}y^2 + 2xy - 8z$
4) $z + w - \frac{1}{y}$
5) $wz^2 + \frac{x + y}{2z}$
6) $z(z - 4w)$
7) $\frac{3 + z}{3 - z}$
8) $8x^2 + \frac{1}{2}y - 4wyz^3$
9) $1 + \frac{12}{y} + \frac{1}{2}xz$
10) $\frac{w^2yz}{4z + y}$

d

If $f = \frac{3}{4}$, $g = -2$, $h = \frac{1}{2}$, $j = 4$, find the values of

1) $2j - 3g$
2) $6h + fj + 2g$
3) $g(3h + f) + j$
4) $f^2 - h^2$
5) $5g^2 + 2g - j^2$
6) $\frac{2j + 3g}{6h + 4f}$
7) $3hg - \frac{1}{2}gj$
8) $2g^2 - jgh$
9) $\frac{4h - \frac{1}{2}fj^2}{hj}$
10) $j^2h^3 - 2f^2$

e

If $k = -3$, $m = 2\frac{1}{4}$, $t = 4$, $v = -1$, find the values of

1) $\frac{kt}{v} - 4m$
2) $k + 3v^3$
3) $3tv + 2m$
4) $\frac{t + v}{v - k}$
5) $4(2m + k) - v$
6) $t + (m - 2)^2$
7) $\frac{k^2}{m}$
8) $\frac{kv + t}{12m - 5t}$
9) $m(v + k - t)$
10) $tv - kt - kv$

A =EQUATIONS

*To solve an equation, the value of the letter must be found.

*In an equation, the terms on the left of the EQUALS SIGN(=) always have the same value (are the same size) as the terms on the right of the equals sign.

e.g. Find the value of N if 4N = 12. $4N = 12$

1) 4 times N equals 12, so **N equals 12 divided by 4** $N = 12/4$

2) N equals 3 $N = 3$

*Notice that ×4 becomes ÷4 when it appears on the other side of the =

---

e.g. Solve the equation	e.g. Solve for a	e.g. Solve for p
$30 = 5y$	$4a = 3$	$2p = 7$
$30/5 = y$	$a = 3/4$	$p = 7/2$
$6 = y$		$p = 3\frac{1}{2}$
$y = 6$		

ALWAYS set out new line of working BELOW previous line with = sign DIRECTLY BELOW = sign.

B

e.g. Find the value of w if $w/4 = 8$. $w/4 = 8$

1) w ÷ 4 equals 8, so **w equals 8 multiplied by 4** $w = 8 \times 4$

2) w equals 32 $\mathbf{w = 32}$

*Notice that ÷4 becomes ×4 when it appears on the other side of the =

---

e.g. Solve for a	e.g. Solve for f	e.g. Solve for i
$\frac{a}{3} = 1$	$f/8 = 3/2$	$\frac{1}{4}i = 5$
$a = 1 \times 3$	$f = 3/2 \times 8$	$i = 5 \times 4$
$a = 3$	$f = 12$	$i = 20$

C

Fractions

$\frac{1}{2}N$ is better written as $N/2$

$\frac{1}{3}x$ is better written as $x/3$

$\frac{1}{5}M$ is better written as $M/5$

a

Solve these equations (Find the value of each letter).
ALWAYS SET OUT EACH NEW LINE OF WORKING **BELOW** PREVIOUS LINE, WITH = SIGN **DIRECTLY BELOW** = SIGN.

1) $4a = 8$
2) $5t = 5$
3) $3g = 15$
4) $2B = 14$
5) $6j = 18$
6) $2x = 6$
7) $4h = 16$
8) $7c = 7$
9) $3K = 24$
10) $2z = 20$
11) $3q = 12$
12) $9L = 18$
13) $11A = 55$
14) $3v = 27$
15) $5e = 35$
16) $2k = 32$
17) $8w = 24$
18) $2U = 12$
19) $3c = 33$
20) $6y = 36$

b

Solve these equations

1) $8y = 56$
2) $3m = 9$
3) $30 = 15d$
4) $3B = 2$
5) $8p = 8$
6) $2u = 5$
7) $7D = 63$
8) $12q = 48$
9) $2E = 1$
10) $5x = 25$
11) $48 = 8M$
12) $4f = 3$
13) $3P = 39$
14) $6A = 54$
15) $3G = 10$
16) $20y = 100$
17) $4w = 25$
18) $5c = 1$
19) $2a = 11$
20) $6H = 66$

c

Solve these equations

1) $B/4 = 2$
2) $N/2 = 10$
3) $a/5 = 1$
4) $e/3 = 3$
5) $x/2 = 21$
6) $V/10 = 4$
7) $T/6 = 2$
8) $C/4 = 14$
9) $F/7 = 3$
10) $S/12 = 1$
11) $D/5 = 4$
12) $h/8 = 8$
13) $A/6 = 0$
14) $b/22 = 3$
15) $w/3 = 5$

d

Solve these equations. Remember that $\frac{1}{3}y$ is the same as $y/3$, etc.

1) $W/3 = 9$
2) $\frac{1}{4}R = 3$
3) $\frac{1}{8}H = 3$
4) $P/2 = 15$
5) $\frac{1}{5}d = 7$
6) $\frac{1}{3}F = 0$
7) $\frac{1}{2}n = 50$
8) $\frac{1}{10}T = 8$
9) $\frac{1}{6}M = 2$
10) $\frac{1}{4}z = 5\frac{1}{2}$

e

Find the value of the letter in each of these equations.

1) $7N = 77$
2) $4j = 34$
3) $R/7 = 6$
4) $8F = 96$
5) $\frac{1}{3}U = 1$
6) $L/2 = 4\frac{1}{2}$
7) $11x = 88$
8) $\frac{1}{5}P = 3.2$
9) $9a = 36$
10) $3C = 7.8$
11) $\frac{1}{12}k = 0.6$
12) $6f = 150$
13) $28 = 4V$
14) $D/2 = 0.9$
15) $5q = 85$
16) $360 = 10h$
17) $\frac{1}{3}S = \frac{1}{3}$
18) $W/14 = 1$
19) $\frac{1}{8}m = \frac{3}{4}$
20) $0.6B = 12$

A = EQUATIONS (2)

e.g. Find the value of A if $A+3=7$

$$A + 3 = 7$$

1) A add 3 equals 7, so
   A equals 7 subtract 3

$$A = 7 - 3$$

2) A equals 4

$$\underline{A = 4}$$

*Notice that +3 becomes −3 when it appears on the other side of the =

---

e.g. Solve the equation $t+6=1$

$$t + 6 = 1$$
$$t = 1 - 6$$
$$\underline{t = -5}$$

B

e.g. Solve the equation $w - 8 = 11$

$$w - 8 = 11$$

1) w subtract 8 equals 11, so
   w equals 11 add 8

$$w = 11 + 8$$

2) w equals 19

$$\underline{w = 19}$$

*Notice that −8 becomes +8 when it appears on the other side of the =

C Checking

The answer to an equation can always be checked by **SUBSTITUTING** the answer for the letter

e.g. Solve the equation $k + 9 = 16$. Answer $\underline{k = \mathbf{7}}$

To check, substitute 7 for k

$$\mathbf{7} + 9 = 16$$

If both sides are equal, your answer is correct.

D Signs

1) The answer should always be written with the letter first,
   e.g. $y = 6$ (not $6 = y$)
2) If the letter comes out as a **minus**,
   change the sides to make it **plus**.
   Then write answer correctly (if necessary)

e.g.

$$-B = 9$$
$$-9 = B$$
$$\underline{B = -9}$$

a

Solve these equations (find the value of each letter).
ALWAYS SET OUT EACH NEW LINE OF WORKING **BELOW** PREVIOUS LINE, WITH = SIGN **DIRECTLY BELOW** = SIGN.

1) $y + 4 = 9$
2) $c + 3 = 11$
3) $f + 1 = 4$
4) $H + 7 = 8$
5) $p + 5 = 3$
6) $x + 1\frac{1}{2} = 6$
7) $R + 9 = 9$
8) $N + 3 = -2$
9) $M + 8.6 = 11.3$
10) $T + 8 = 0$
11) $j + 0 = 15$
12) $P + 6 = 1$
13) $2 + E = 7$
14) $0.4 + n = 2.7$
15) $Q + 7 = -4$

b

Solve these equations

1) $B - 6 = 5$
2) $k - 1 = 1$
3) $W - 3 = 4$
4) $s - 12 = 10$
5) $e - 2 = 8$
6) $n - 3 = 0$
7) $Y - 7 = -5$
8) $a - 8 = 1$
9) $G - 1 = -8$
10) $M - 1.4 = 3.8$
11) $d - \frac{1}{2} = 3$
12) $h - 5 = -9$
13) $r - 21 = 0$
14) $U - 7 = -2$
15) $c - \frac{1}{4} = \frac{1}{2}$

c

Write down the value of N in each of these. Your answer each time should begin N =

1) $5 = N$
2) $-N = 7$
3) $-2 = N$
4) $-N = -10$
5) $6 = 2N$
6) $8 - N = 3$
7) $7 = N + 1$
8) $42 = N/6$
9) $14 = N - 5$
10) $-N = 12$
11) $3 = 4 - N$
12) $11 = -N - 8$
13) $1.6 + N = 2.5$
14) $7 = N + 12$
15) $4 - N = -4$
16) $-5 = N/3$
17) $-4N = 48$
18) $63 = 7N$
19) $9\frac{1}{2} - N = 0$
20) $2 = N/11$

d

Solve these equations. Make sure your answer is written with the letter first, e.g. m = 3.

1) $x - 8 = 20$
2) $c + 3 = 5$
3) $u - 7 = 2$
4) $K + 33 = 40$
5) $8 + G = 3$
6) $7 - q = 1$
7) $30 = d + 25$
8) $H - 11 = -4$
9) $3\frac{1}{2} + p = 8$
10) $A - 2 = -10$
11) $x + 7.55 = 10.3$
12) $t - 7 = 0$
13) $12 + B = 1$
14) $e - 2 = -1$
15) $6 - y = 8$

A = EQUATIONS (3)

e.g. Solve for N $3N + 4 = 19$

*1) Collect all LETTER terms on one side of the = sign, and all the other terms on the other side $3N = 19 \quad 4$

*2) Make **signs** correct $3N = 19 - 4$

*3) Work out both sides $3N = 15$

*4) Finish off $N = {}^{15}\!/_{3}$

$\underline{N = 5}$

---

e.g. Solve for y

$$2y - 5 = 21$$
$$2y = 21 + 5$$
$$2y = 26$$
$$y = {}^{26}\!/_{2}$$
$$\underline{y = 13}$$

e.g. Find the value of a

$$a/3 + 5 = 9$$
$$a/3 = 9 - 5$$
$$a/3 = 4$$
$$a = 4 \times 3$$
$$\underline{a = 12}$$

B

Signs. It is sometimes easier, if you prefer, to start with the LETTER TERMS on the right-hand side of the = sign.

e.g.
$$11 - 4x = 3$$
$$11 - 3 = 4x$$
$$8 = 4x$$
$$2 = x$$
$$\underline{x = 2}$$

C

Brackets. If an equation contains brackets, multiply out the brackets first.

e.g.
$$3(h - 4) = 15$$
$$3h - 12 = 15$$
$$3h = 27$$
$$\underline{h = 9}$$

e.g.
$$2(5 - 3N) = 34$$
$$10 - 6N = 34$$
$$10 - 34 = 6N$$
$$-24 = 6N$$
$$-4 = N$$
$$\underline{N = -4}$$

a Solve these equations

1) $2v + 5 = 7$
2) $4m + 1 = 25$
3) $3F - 2 = 10$
4) $5 + 6c = 23$
5) $2Q - 19 = 13$
6) $\frac{1}{2}N + 3 = 5$
7) $3e - 6 = 0$
8) $2k - 11 = 2$
9) $5T + 5 = 30$
10) $x/2 - 4 = 3$
11) $8h - \frac{1}{2} = 7\frac{1}{2}$
12) $6L + 8 = 8$
13) $2b - 25 = 13$
14) $G/4 + 6 = 9$
15) $50 = 24S + 2$

---

b Solve these equations

1) $8 + 11p = 63$
2) $Y/9 - 1 = 1$
3) $12 - 2j = 4$
4) $1 - 3a = -8$
5) $2 + u/2 = 7$
6) $\frac{1}{3}K + 5 = 14$
7) $6r - 9 = 0$
8) $15 = 3 + 2H$
9) $3 - 4f = 1$
10) $d/8 + 6 = 12$
11) $8 = 11 - M/5$
12) $V + 8 = -3$
13) $1 + \frac{1}{4}n = 0$
14) $E/12 - 6 = -4$
15) $6 - 5Z = 31$

---

c Solve these equations

1) $4(w + 5) = 24$
2) $3(z - 7) = 6$
3) $5(c + 2) = 0$
4) $2(1 + y) = 12$
5) $6(4 - B) = 6$
6) $4(t - \frac{1}{2}) = 14$
7) $2(2m + 3) = 34$
8) $3(4x - 10) = 66$
9) $20 = 2(D + 4)$
10) $5(6 + R) = 35$
11) $4(J + \frac{1}{2}) = 10$
12) $7(\frac{1}{2} + e) = 7$
13) $9 = 3(U - 10)$
14) $5(3f - 2) = 35$
15) $\frac{1}{2}(4v + 6) = 11$

---

d Solve these equations

1) $2(1 + 6P) = 26$
2) $\frac{1}{3}(3x - 12) = 7$
3) $2(4N + 5) = 12$
4) $6(w/3 + 1) = 24$
5) $4(3 - L) = 0$
6) $3(3r + 1) = -15$
7) $5(2 - E) = 30$
8) $7 = 2(\frac{1}{2}b - 9)$
9) $12(K/4 - \frac{1}{2}) = 0$
10) $1 = 2(6c - 1)$
11) $9(2 + y/3) = 6$
12) $\frac{1}{2}(10 + 8T) = 37$
13) $-3(5 + 2A) = 15$
14) $2 = -4(d - 3)$
15) $10(\frac{1}{2} - h) = 4$

A $><$ INEQUALITIES

1) **Inequalities** are the same as equations, except that the left-hand side of the inequality sign is NOT EQUAL to the right-hand side.

2) **Signs for inequalities are**

$>$ is greater than
$<$ is less than
$\geqslant$ is greater than or equal to
$\leqslant$ is less than or equal to

3) Inequalities are solved exactly the same way as equations, e.g.

$$3w < 24 \qquad\qquad k/4 - 7 \geqslant 3$$
$$w < 24/3 \qquad\qquad k/4 \geqslant 3 + 7$$
$$\underline{w < 8} \qquad\qquad k/4 \geqslant 10$$
$$\underline{k \geqslant 40}$$

REMEMBER -2 is greater than -3
-3 is less than -2, etc.

B GREATEST & LEAST POSSIBLE VALUE

e.g. If x is a whole number (an integer), what is the greatest possible value of x if $4x + 3 < 17$?

The answer comes to $x < 3\frac{1}{2}$ (x is less than $3\frac{1}{2}$) so the **greatest** possible value of x is **3.**

If the answer to an inequality came to $c > 5\frac{1}{4}$, the **least** possible whole number value for c would be **6.**

C

BE CAREFUL about the last lines of working

e.g. If the inequality comes out $\quad -y < 5$

*1) Change sides to get the value of y $\quad -5 < y$

*2) Write the answer the correct way round $\quad \underline{y > -5}$

Notice that the SIGN changes round too.

e.g.

$$2 - a > -5$$
$$2 + 5 > a$$
$$7 > a$$
$$\underline{a < 7}$$

e.g.

$$2 - 3d \leqslant 14$$
$$2 - 14 \leqslant 3d$$
$$-12 \leqslant 3d$$
$$-4 \leqslant d$$
$$\underline{d \geqslant -4}$$

a

Solve these inequalities

1) $3x < 9$
2) $5w > 5$
3) $2c \geqslant 8$
4) $Z + 1 < 7$
5) $J/4 \leqslant 3$
6) $m - 8 > 9$
7) $S/3 < 7$
8) $G + 6 < 2$
9) $2n - 2 \leqslant 9$
10) $6u - 2 \geqslant 28$
11) $4F + 5 > 11$
12) $9 + 2q \leqslant 3$
13) $R/5 + 8 > 12$
14) $2k - 13 < 4$
15) $6(p - 7) \leqslant 12$

b

Solve these inequalities

1) $4 - A \geqslant 3$
2) $12 < c + 5$
3) $6 - M < 0$
4) $19 - 4e > 3$
5) $5 \geqslant 8 + B$
6) $4(3 + k) > 8$
7) $7 < 3f - 5$
8) $3H - 4 < -3$
9) $8(V/4 - 1) \geqslant 24$
10) $1 \leqslant 2p + 13$
11) $3(D + 7) > 12$
12) $21 \geqslant 6w + 6$
13) $12b - 5 < 1$
14) $23 - 2t \leqslant 7$
15) $34 > 2(5 + 2N)$

c

In each of these, N is a whole number. Find the GREATEST POSSIBLE VALUE of N in each.

1) $N < 6\frac{2}{3}$
2) $N < 4\frac{1}{5}$
3) $4N < 10$
4) $3N < 17$
5) $5N < 9$
6) $N - \frac{3}{4} < 3$
7) $4N + 4 < 11$
8) $9 + 6N < 60$
9) $5N < 27$
10) $8N - 7 < 9$
11) $6 - N > 2.5$
12) $4N + 14 < 2$
13) $1 + 2N < 20$
14) $9 > 3N - 4$
15) $-11 > N - 6$

d

In each of these, y is a whole number. Find the LEAST POSSIBLE VALUE of y in each.

1) $y > 4\frac{1}{2}$
2) $2y > 15$
3) $3y > 38$
4) $y > -5\frac{1}{2}$
5) $4y > 7$
6) $5y + 3 > 25$
7) $7y - 8 > 38$
8) $6y - 1 > 0$
9) $12 - y < 4.2$
10) $1\frac{1}{2} + 2y > 23$
11) $14 < 4y + 1$
12) $y/2 + 8 > 13$
13) $3y - 5 > -17$
14) $2 - 6y < 21$
15) $5y + 12 > 1$

A EQUATIONS AND INEQUALITIES

e.g. Solve for y	$5(2y + 3) - y = y - 1$
*1) Multiply out brackets (if any)	$10y + 15 - y = y - 1$
*2) All LETTER terms on one side of = or inequality sign. All other terms on other side.	$10y \quad y \quad y = 1 \quad 15$
*3) Put in correct signs **BE VERY CAREFUL!** A plus quantity appearing on the other side becomes MINUS; a minus quantity becomes PLUS	$10y - y - y = -1 - 15$
*4) Work out each side	$8y = -16$
*5) If letter term is negative (−), change sides and signs	
*6) Finish off	$y = -16/8$ $y = -2$

---

e.g. Solve for n	$3(n + 4) - 4(n - 2) \leqslant 5(n - 3) + 5$
*1) Brackets	$3n + 12 - 4n + 8 \leqslant 5n - 15 + 5$
*2) Letter terms on one side	$3n \quad 4n \quad 5n \leqslant 15 \quad 5 \quad 12 \quad 8$
*3) Correct signs BE VERY CAREFUL!	$3n - 4n - 5n \leqslant -15 + 5 - 12 - 8$
*4) Work out each side	$-6n \leqslant -30$
*5) If letter term is negative (−), change sides and signs	$30 \leqslant 6n$
*6) Finish off	$5 \leqslant n$ $n \geqslant 5$

a

Solve these equations and inequalities.
Keep the = (or inequality) signs **DIRECTLY BELOW** one another.
BE VERY CAREFUL ABOUT THE **SIGNS**!

1) $6a - 7 = 2a + 1$
2) $9 - 2b = b + 14 - 4b$
3) $2c - 11 + 3c - 5 = 6 - 8c + 17$
4) $d - 7 - 5d + 8 = 2 - 3d - 4 + 2d$
5) $5e - 3 + 32 + e = 3e + 1 - 4e$
6) $1 + 7f + 4f - 9 = f - 5 + 8f - 3$
7) $2g - 15 + 4g + 5 < 22 + 3g - 8$
8) $h + 10 - 3h - 7 = -6h + 8 + 5h - 4$
9) $4j - 5 + 6j \geqslant 18 - j + 5j - 2$
10) $-13 + 3k - 6k + 7 < 4k - 3 - 2k + 9 - 7k$

b

Solve these equations and inequalities

1) $3(m - 6) + 5 = 2(m + 1)$
2) $5 + 4(n - 2) \geqslant 2(2n + 3) - 3n$
3) $3(4p - 3) - 3p < 7(2 + p) - 1$
4) $5q + 7 - 4(1 - q) = 6(2q + 3)$
5) $r - 2(3 + r) = 4(1 - 2r) + 4$
6) $2(3s - 5) + 7 > 11 - 3(4 - s)$
7) $4t + 4(2t - 3) - 3(t - 10) = 0$
8) $9 + 2(6 - 3u) > 5(u - 1) + 2u$
9) $3(v + 3) - 2(3 + v) \leqslant 7 - (v + 5)$
10) $9 = 6(w - 1) - 2(w + 5) + w$

c

In each of these, m is an integer. Find the LEAST possible value of m in each.

1) $4m - 3 + m + 7 > 15 - 2m$
2) $8(m + 1) - 5(m - 4) - m > 7$
3) $5m - 2(4 - 2m) > 3(m + 6)$
4) $2(m - 3) + 4m > m + 8$
5) $6 + 4(2m - 3) < 3(4m - 5)$

d

In each of these, x is an integer. Find the GREATEST possible value of x in each.

1) $x + 12 + 7x - 9 < 2x + 22$
2) $3 < 4(8 - 2x) - (x - 20)$
3) $4(\frac{1}{2}x + 1) - 3(x - 8) < 2(\frac{1}{2} - 4x)$
4) $4 - 2(x + 1) + 4x > 3x - 10$
5) $6(4 - x) + 7(x - 2) < 5(12 - x)$

A EQUATIONS AND INEQUALITIES WITH FRACTIONS

e.g. Solve for x $\frac{3x}{4} - 2 = \frac{2x}{3}$

*1) Find the Lowest Common Denominator of the fractions —— (12)

*2) Multiply ALL the terms by the lowest Common Denominator $\frac{3x \times 12}{4} - 2 \times 12 = \frac{2x \times 12}{3}$

*3) Cancel in each term if possible $\frac{3x \times \cancel{12}^{3}}{\cancel{4}_{1}} - 2 \times 12 = \frac{2x \times \cancel{12}^{4}}{\cancel{3}_{1}}$

*4) Finish off

$$9x - 24 = 8x$$
$$9x - 8x = 24$$
$$\underline{x = 24}$$

B

e.g. Solve for a $\frac{2a+1}{2} - \frac{a-2}{3} < 4\frac{1}{2}$

*1) Put brackets round any numerator with two or more terms $\frac{(2a+1)}{2} - \frac{(a-2)}{3} < 4\frac{1}{2}$

*2) Find Lowest Common Denominator —— (6)

*3) Multiply all terms by L.C.D.

*4) Cancel

$$\frac{{}^{3}\cancel{6}(2a+1)}{\cancel{2}_{1}} - \frac{{}^{2}\cancel{6}(a-2)}{\cancel{3}_{1}} < \frac{9}{\cancel{2}_{1}} \times \frac{\cancel{6}^{3}}{1}$$

*5) Finish off (MIND SIGNS!)

$$6a + 3 - 2a + 4 < 27$$
$$4a < 20$$
$$\underline{a < 5}$$

C

CROSS MULTIPLICATION

If each side of an equation or inequality is a SINGLE FRACTION, cross multiplication can be used.

e.g. $\frac{3x}{4} = \frac{7}{8}$

$$\frac{3x}{\mathbf{4}} \rightleftarrows \frac{7}{\mathbf{8}}$$

$$\mathbf{8} \times 3x = \mathbf{4} \times 7$$
$$24x = 28$$
$$\underline{x = 1\frac{1}{6}}$$

e.g. $\frac{4(x-1)}{5} = \frac{2x}{3}$

$$\frac{4(x-1)}{\mathbf{5}} \rightleftarrows \frac{2x}{\mathbf{3}}$$

$$\mathbf{3} \times 4(x-1) = \mathbf{5} \times 2x$$
$$12x - 12 = 10x$$
$$\underline{x = 6}$$

a Solve these equations

1) $\frac{a}{4} + \frac{a}{2} = 9$

2) $\frac{d+2}{2} - \frac{d}{3} = 2$

3) $\frac{y}{4} + \frac{y-5}{3} = 10$

4) $\frac{R}{3} + \frac{R}{6} = \frac{1}{2} + \frac{R}{4}$

5) $\frac{p+3}{5} - \frac{p}{4} = 0$

6) $\frac{x-4}{5} + \frac{1}{2} = \frac{x+4}{10}$

7) $\frac{2J}{3} - 2 = \frac{J-4}{3}$

8) $\frac{1}{2} + \frac{U}{3} = \frac{U}{6}$

9) $\frac{m+5}{6} - \frac{m-1}{8} = 1\frac{1}{2}$

10) $\frac{2H+1}{5} + \frac{H+5}{3} = H$

b Solve these equations

1) $3 + \frac{f-1}{4} = 10 - \frac{f+1}{2}$

2) $\frac{k}{5} + 7 = 3k$

3) $\frac{N+1}{9} - \frac{1}{12} = \frac{N}{6}$

4) $7 - \frac{q}{3} = \frac{3q+3}{2}$

5) $1 = \frac{m-4}{3} - \frac{m+3}{5}$

6) $\frac{W}{4} - 2 = \frac{W}{6}$

7) $j - 6 = 2 + \frac{3j}{7}$

8) $\frac{2x-7}{3} - x = \frac{x+6}{5} - 1$

9) $\frac{A}{3} + 2 = \frac{1}{2}(A+1)$

10) $3\frac{1}{2} - \frac{2L-1}{8} = \frac{2L+1}{4}$

c Solve these inequalities

1) $\frac{V-1}{2} + \frac{V+1}{6} > 1$

2) $2t - 7 \leqslant \frac{5(t-2)}{4}$

3) $3 < \frac{Q+2}{7} + \frac{Q-1}{2}$

4) $\frac{h-3}{2} - \frac{5h+1}{12} > \frac{h-1}{3}$

5) $\frac{5x}{4} - \frac{3x+4}{8} \geqslant \frac{x+2}{2}$

6) $\frac{4-e}{9} < e - \frac{3e+1}{6}$

7) $20 - i > \frac{3i}{2} + 5$

8) $\frac{c+4}{3} - \frac{2c+5}{2} \geqslant c + \frac{1}{2}$

9) $3(2+n) < \frac{n-1}{4} - 7\frac{1}{2}$

10) $\frac{1}{4}B - \frac{2B-5}{12} \leqslant \frac{B-1}{3}$

A FORMULAE

Think of a number and call it n

e.g.

1) Multiply it by 7. The result is $7n$
2) Divide it by 5. The result is $n/5$
3) Add 3 to it. The result is $(n + 3)$
4) Subtract 6 from it. The result is $(n - 6)$
5) Subtract it from 9. The result is $(9 - n)$

---

6) Multiply it by 4, and then subtract 5. The result is $(4n - 5)$
7) Add 7 to it, and then divide by 2. The result is $\left(\frac{n+7}{2}\right)$
8) Divide it by 6, and then add 11. The result is $\left(\frac{n}{6} + 11\right)$
9) Subtract 3 from it, and then multiply by 8.
The result is $8(n - 3)$, etc.

Some examples

1) What is the cost of 7 bananas at 2h pence each? 14h pence
2) Paul is 3 years older than Amanda. If Amanda is A years old, how old is Paul? Paul is $(A + 3)$ years old.
3) Each packet contains $(C - 5)$ biscuits. How many biscuits are there in 18 packets? $18(C - 5)$
4) A pencil costs y pence less than a pen. If the pen costs 14 pence, how much does the pencil cost?
The pencil costs $(14 - y)$ pence
5) A businessman owned W oil-wells. His daughter owned 4 more oil-wells than her father. How many did they own altogether?
Businessman owned W oil-wells
Daughter owned $(W + 4)$ oil-wells, so
altogether they owned $W + (W + 4) = (2W + 4)$ oil-wells

B

Consecutive numbers are whole numbers which follow one another, e.g. 6,7,8,9,10 are consecutive numbers.
The next consecutive numbers above n are
$(n + 1)$, $(n + 2)$, etc.
The next consecutive numbers below n are
$(n - 1)$, $(n - 2)$, etc.

a Find the cost of

1) y sausages at 4 pence each
2) 10 computers at £J each
3) ½ a kilogram of sugar at z pence a kilogram
4) 6 magazines at (V + 2) pence each
5) 5 buns at n pence and n buns at 8 pence each

6) Mary is x years old now. How old will she be in 4 years from now?
7) Katherine is 130 centimetres tall. David is t centimetres taller than Katherine. How tall is David?
8) What are the next three consecutive numbers above y?
9) Mr Anderson owned h hectares of land. Mr Briggs owned a quarter of Mr Anderson's amount, and Mr Craggs owned three times Mr Anderson's amount. How much land did Mr Briggs own and how much land did Mr Craggs own?
10) John is 10 years old now. How old was he M years ago?

---

b

1) Find the next three consecutive numbers below (k + 1).
2) One month, Ann saved £G, and Christine saved £5 more than Ann saved. How much money did they save altogether?
3) During a hockey season James scored d goals, Roger scored 2 less than James, and Sarah scored 6 more than James. How many goals did they score altogether?
4) The difference in height between two mountains was 900 metres. If the higher one was R metres high, how high was the lower one?
5) Rachel and Emily shared c chips. If Emily had 27 of them, how many had Rachel?
6) A bus travelled by motorway from Yorwell to High Mill, a distance of q miles. Then it returned to Yorwell by a route which was 6 miles longer. How far did it go altogether?
7) Robert had n model cars. George had 7 more than twice the number of cars Robert had. How many had George?
8) There were p people living in the village of Yewham. In another village, Exton, there was exactly half this number of people. A third village, called Wybury, had 120 more people than Exton had. How many people lived in Wybury?
9) Deborah collected d conkers, and Heather collected h conkers. Heather added her collection to Deborah's and then they shared the total equally. What was each girl's share?
10) Of the z baboons in Bengleton Zoo, (z − 4) are female. How many are male?

A FORMULAE (2)

A **FORMULA** is a short way, using letters, of writing a sentence. Formulae contain numbers, letters and signs, but NOT UNITS.

e.g. The area of a rectangle is calculated by multiplying together the length and the width.

This can be written as a formula $A = LW$

*A (the area) is the SUBJECT of the formula

*A is expressed IN TERMS OF L (the length) and W (the width)

---

e.g. Andrew sets off from home to visit his aunt who lives 15 miles away. When he has gone m miles, how far has he still to go?

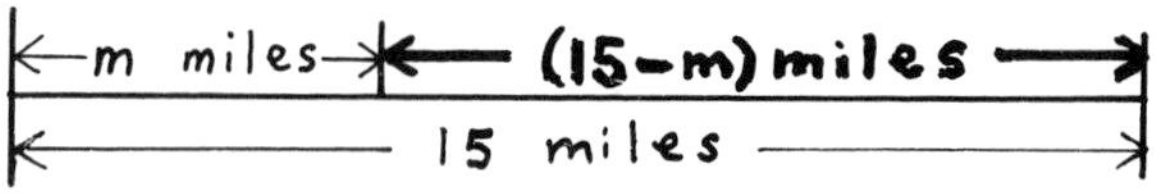

He still has to go (15 − m) miles

Write a formula showing the distance D which he still has to go

$$D = 15 - m$$

*D is the subject of the formula.

*D is expressed in terms of m.

---

e.g. A rectangle has a length L and a width W. The perimeter of a rectangle is twice the length plus twice the width. Write a formula for calculating the perimeter P of a rectangle.

$$P = 2L + 2W$$

---

e.g. At MacLeod's the Greengrocers, grapefruit cost 20 pence each and lemons cost 14 pence each. Write a formula for finding the total cost T, in pence, of G grapefruit and L lemons.

$$T = 20G + 14L$$

---

e.g. Sally was given n pence spending money. Amy was given half the amount that Sally was given. Write a formula showing Amy's spending money A.

$$A = n/2$$

a

1) The volume of a cuboid can be found by multiplying together its length L, its width W and its height H. Write a formula for finding the volume V of a cuboid, beginning V =

2) Bert set off from his home to drive to Portsmouth which was 29 miles away. How far from Portsmouth was he after he had driven M miles?

3) A man is paid £5 an hour for working normal hours and £8 an hour for working overtime. Construct a formula for calculating the man's pay P if he worked n normal hours and x hours of overtime.

4) Whenever Emma buys s sweets, she gives r of them to Rebecca and c of them to Christopher. Write a formula to calculate the number E of sweets she has left after she has shared them out.

5) The area of a triangle can be calculated by multiplying half the base b by the height h. Using this information, write a formula for calculating (i) the area a of a triangle, and (ii) the area A of a regular hexagon like the one shown in the drawing.

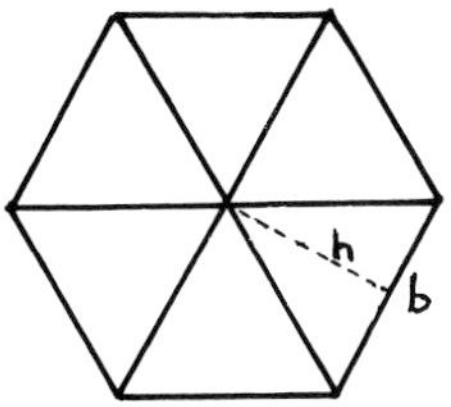

6) Write a formula for finding the sum s of five consecutive numbers, the smallest of which is n.

7) One way of expressing a number of gallons G as a number of litres L is to multiply the number of gallons by 50 and divide the result by 11. Write, the shortest possible way, a formula for converting gallons into litres, beginning L =

8) A tank was filled with 25000 cubic centimetres of water. Each day 200 cubic centimetres of water leaked out of the tank. Write a formula to find the volume V of water left in the tank after d days.

9) For each journey by taxi, a taxi-driver charges 75 pence, and then an extra 50 pence for each mile of the journey. Write a formula for calculating the cost C of a journey in terms of the distance m in miles.

10) Uncle Alastair always gives Rachel money for her birthday. He calculates the number of pounds he gives her by halving her age and adding 5. Write a formula to show the number of pounds A he gives her when she becomes y years old.

A FORMULAE (3)

Solving equations

e.g. John got J marks in a test. Lucy got 4 more marks than John.

1) How many marks did they get altogether?

John		Lucy	
J	+	(J + 4)	= (2J + 4) marks

2) The total of their marks was 30. Form an equation and solve for J.

$$2J + 4 = 30$$
$$2J = 26$$
$$\underline{J = 13}$$

---

e.g. A box contained green apples and red apples. There were 15 more green apples than there were red apples.

Altogether there were 47 apples. How many green apples were there?

1) Let g be the number of green apples

2) Altogether there were

Green		Red	
g	+	(g − 15)	= (2g − 15) apples

This gives the equation

$$2g - 15 = 47$$
$$2g = 62$$
$$\underline{g = 31}$$

<u>There were 31 green apples.</u>

---

e.g. Bryan thought of a number. He took 4 away from it and multiplied the result by 6. He ended up with 42. What was the number he first thought of?

1) Let N be the number he first thought of

2) He took 4 away from it $\quad N - 4$

3) He multiplied the result by 6 $\quad 6(N - 4)$

4) He ended up with 42 $\quad 6(N - 4) = 42$

$$6N - 24 = 42$$
$$6N = 66$$
$$\underline{N = 11}$$

<u>11 was the number he first thought of.</u>

a

1) Find the sum of $(a + 1)$ and $(a - 6)$. Make your answer equal to 35, and solve for a.

2) Colin and David between them ate 15 toffees. Colin ate t of the toffees; David ate $(t - 3)$ of them. How many did Colin eat?

3) Add together z, $(z-4)$ and $(z-9)$. Make the total equal to 17 and solve for z.

4) Three sisters have ages x years, $(x+2)$ years and $(x+5)$ years. The total of their ages is 34 years. How old is the youngest sister?

5) Four consecutive numbers add up to 62. What are they? (Clue. Let N be the lowest of the four numbers).

6) A balloon man sold red balloons and blue balloons. One morning he sold q red balloons and $(q-12)$ blue balloons. How many did he sell altogether? If he sold 54 balloons altogether, how many red ones did he sell?

7) Neil went on a three-day walking holiday. The first day he walked d miles, the second day $(d+11)$ miles, and the third day $(d-6)$ miles. If he walked a total of 68 miles, what distance did he walk on the first day?

8) Tracy saved £6x. Then she spent £ $(x+7)$ of her savings on a new camera. After buying the camera, she had £33 of her savings left. Make an equation, solve for x, and calculate the cost of the camera.

9) In a cricket match, Iain scored r runs, Douglas scored 5 more than Iain, and Rory scored 6 less than Iain. Altogether they scored 41. What was Iain's score?

10) John bought 3 pencils at $(c-7)$ pence each, a ruler at c pence and 2 sharpeners at $(c+5)$ pence each. He spent 73 pence altogether. Find the cost of the ruler.

11) Tom thought of a number. He multiplied it by 4 and then took away 18. The final answer was the number he first thought of. What was the number?

12) At a summer camp there were 7 more girls than there were boys. There were 63 boys and girls altogether. How many boys were there?

13) The three numbers 2e, $(e+5)$ and $(e+2)$ add up to 59. What are the three numbers?

14) Pauline and Alison live in the same road. If you subtract 25 from the number of Alison's house and multiply the result by 3, you get Pauline's house number which is 57. What number is Alison's house?

15) Paul is p years old. His father is 3 times Paul's age. Find the ages of Paul and his father 6 years ago. Six years ago, Paul's Father's age was 5 times Paul's age. How old is Paul now?

A FORMULAE (4)

Substitution

Substitution means replacing, or substituting, letters with numbers, so that the answer (the VALUE) comes out as a number *(see page 34).*

e.g. Find the value of D in the formula $D = 80n$ when $n = 7$.
*Replace the letter with the correct number

$$D = 80 \times 7$$
$$\underline{D = 560}$$

---

e.g. Find the value of v in the formula $v = 2s + c$ when $s = 9$ and $c = 12$.

*Replace the letters with the correct numbers.
Use brackets, if necessary, to make working clearer

$$v = (2 \times 9) + 12$$
$$v = 18 + 12$$
$$\underline{v = 30}$$

---

e.g. In the formula $a = 4b - c$ find b when $a = 13$ and $c = 1$.

$$a = 4b - c$$
$$13 = 4b - 1$$
$$13 + 1 = 4b$$
$$14 = 4b$$
$$\underline{b = 3\tfrac{1}{2}}$$

---

e.g. Find s in the formula $s = ut + \frac{1}{2}ft^2$ when $f = -32$, $u = 15$, $t = 4$

$$s = ut + \tfrac{1}{2}ft^2$$
$$s = (15 \times 4) + (\tfrac{1}{2} \times -32 \times 4 \times 4)$$
$$s = 60 - 256$$
$$\underline{s = -196}$$

a

1) If $C = 75 + 10d$, find the value of C when $d = 14$
2) In the formula $v = s^3$ find v when $s = 7$
3) Find t in the formula $t = \frac{h + 2m}{7}$ when $h = 25$, $m = 33$
4) If $B = 25c + 15d$, find B when $c = 16$, $d = 3$
5) If $J = 4q^2 - 3r$, find J when $q = 3$ and $r = 12$
6) If $E = 1300 + 7.5u$, find the value of E when $u = 250$
7) In the formula $\frac{PV}{T} = k$, find the value of k when $P = 75$, $V = 120$, $T = 15$
8) Find S in the formula $S = 9P + 8R$ when $P = 8$ and $R = -1\frac{1}{2}$
9) Find I in the formula $I = \frac{PRT}{100}$ when $P = 2500$, $R = 8.5$, $T = 4$
10) If $A = 2(LW + LH + WH)$, find A when $L = 16$, $W = 10$, and $H = 6.5$

---

b

1) If $v = u + ft$, find v when $u = 25$, $f = 5$, $t = 12$
2) In the formula $p = 5d/12$ find p when $d = 102$
3) Find F when $C = -40$ in the formula $F = 9C/5 + 32$
4) In the formula $Z = \frac{W}{W+Y}$ find Z where $W = 48$, $Y = 12$
5) Find q in the formula $e = 2w + 4pq$ if $e = 200$, $w = 250$, $p = -5$
6) If $a = \frac{bc}{d}$, find a when $b = 1.2$, $c = 3.25$, $d = 0.6$
7) Find the value of W in the formula $W = V^2/R$ when $V = 12$, $R = 90$
8) If $C = 2\pi r$, find C when $\pi = 3.14$ and $r = 15$
9) From the equation $F = 7/10\,d - 6e$ find F when $d = 25$ and $e = \frac{3}{4}$
10) Find a in the formula $a = \frac{h}{2}(b + t)$ when $h = 6$, $b = 10.5$, $t = 6.5$
11) If $p = k/v$, find k when $p = 760$, $v = 2.5$
12) Given that $2m + 4n = 15$ find the value of n when $m = 9\frac{1}{2}$
13) Find V in the formula $V = \pi r^2 h$, when $\pi = \frac{22}{7}$, $r = 14$ and $h = 10$
14) In the formula $I = P/d^2$ find P when $I = \frac{2}{3}$ and $d = 6$
15) If $h = \sqrt{a^2 + b^2}$ find h when $a = 5$, $b = 12$

A FORMULAE (5)

Changing the subject of a formula

(Expressing a letter IN TERMS OF another letter).

This is done just like solving an equation.

e.g. Make **d** the subject of the formula $a = 4 - 3\mathbf{d}$

*1) Collect SUBJECT-LETTER terms on one side of = or inequality sign.
All other terms on the other side.
PUT THE SUBJECT-LETTER ON THE SIDE WHERE IT WILL BE POSITIVE (+) $\quad 3\mathbf{d} = 4 \quad a$

*2) Make signs correct $\quad 3\mathbf{d} = 4 - a$

*3) Finish off (by × or ÷ or cross-multiplication) $\quad \mathbf{d} = \dfrac{4 - a}{3}$

---

e.g. Express **y** in terms of x in the formula $x = \dfrac{\mathbf{y}}{2} + 7$

*1) Collect SUBJECT-LETTER terms on one side $\quad x \quad 7 = \dfrac{\mathbf{y}}{2}$

*2) Make signs correct $\quad x - 7 = \dfrac{\mathbf{y}}{2}$

*3) Finish off $\quad 2(x - 7) = \mathbf{y}$

$$\mathbf{y} = 2(x - 7)$$

---

e.g. Make H the subject of the formula

$$4G + 5H = 22$$

$$5H = 22 - 4G$$

$$H = \frac{22 - 4G}{5}$$

e.g. Express t in terms of u and w

$$u < \frac{8w^2t}{3}$$

$$\frac{3u}{8w^2} < t$$

$$t > \frac{3u}{8w^2}$$

REMEMBER

1) Always make sure your final answer STARTS with the subject-letter.

2) Be very careful with $>$, $\geqslant$, $<$ or $\leqslant$ if you swap sides *(see page 46C)*.

a

Make n the subject of the formula in each of these.

1) $p = n - 2$
2) $J = 9 + n$
3) $a = 25 - n$
4) $n + k = W$
5) $x = n/5$
6) $8n = R$
7) $y = 2n - 19$
8) $q - n = t$
9) $z = 15n + y$
10) $7n + 3p = 27$
11) $n/2 - c = 12$
12) $U = 60n - V^2$
13) $\frac{1}{2} < m - 12n$
14) $D = 3n/8$
15) $3f - 22n = 4$

---

b

Express C in terms of A and B in each of these.

1) $B = 4C - A$
2) $A = C/8 + B$
3) $5A = 6B - C$
4) $9C - 35A = B$
5) $B = C + A$
6) $A = BC - 7$
7) $B = 2A + C - 33$
8) $A = CB/6$
9) $AB + 17C = 100$
10) $B = CA^2$

---

c

1) Express m in terms of E and c in the formula $E = mc^2$
2) Make q the subject of the formula $P = 500 - 8q$
3) From the formula $a = \frac{bcd}{100}$ express d in terms of a, b and c.
4) Express E in terms of F and C in the formula $F + C = E + 2$.
5) Make b the subject of the formula $S = \frac{a}{2} + \frac{b}{2}$
6) Express D in terms of S and T in the formula $S = D/T$
7) Make y the subject of the formula $x = 5y - 7z$
8) Make P the subject of the formula $R = Q - \frac{5P}{6}$
9) Express h in terms of k, r and w in the formula
$$k = \frac{3hr}{4} - w.$$
10) Make g the subject of the formula $v = u - gt$.

SOME EXTRA QUESTIONS

1) Simplify (i) $4k - 6k + 3k - 7k$
(ii) $5.3VW - 3.8VW$

2) If $h=2$, $j=3$, $k=0$, find the value of $4hj^2 - 3k^2$

3) Solve for U
$3(2U - 5) = 2(3U + 4) - (U + 8)$

4) (i) Find the sum of $p - 4r$, $4p - 2r$ and $5r - 2p$.
(ii) What must be subtracted from $B + 3A$ to give $A + 2B$?

5) Factorise $8H^2M + 16HM - 12HM^2$ as fully as possible.

6) Patrick had P peppermints. Janice had 9 less peppermints than Patrick. If Patrick then gave 5 of his peppermints to Janice, how many peppermints would Patrick have and how many peppermints would Janice have?

7) From the formula $X = 2Y + 9$
(i) express Y in terms of X
(ii) find the value of X when $Y = 2\frac{1}{2}$

8) Simplify (i) $-cd \times df \times -cef$
(ii) $34gj \div -2j$

9) There were x passengers travelling on a bus. When the bus stopped, 4 passengers got off and 2x got on. Further along the road the bus stopped again and 5 passengers got off and x got on. Write an expression, and simplify it, to show the number of passengers travelling in the bus after the second stop.

10) Solve the equation $\frac{d}{3} - \frac{d}{4} + 10 = \frac{d}{2}$

11) Simplify (i) $6m + 4h + m - 9h$
(ii) $a^3 + 2a^2 - 5a^3 - a^2 + 4a^3$

12) In a quiz, Barbara scored $(n-9)$ points, Sophie scored n points and Tammy scored $(n + 8)$ points. Altogether they scored 65 points. How many points did each person score?

13) Divide $6y^3z^4 + 18yz^2$ by $6yz^2$

14) If D is an integer, find the greatest possible value of D if
$7D - 8 < 5(2D + 3) - 9D$

15) Simplify $\frac{2L-3}{5} - \frac{L+1}{3}$

16) Multiply out (i) $-5(3tv - 5w^2)$
(ii) $\frac{2}{3}(6AC + 15A - 3)$

17) Find the sum of six consecutive numbers, the **largest** of which is N.

18) If $M = 1\frac{1}{2}$, $P = -6$, $Q = 4$ calculate the value of $2MQ + 3MP - 5Q$.

19) Simplify (i) $12 + 3(B - 5)$
(ii) $g(5 + g) - 2g^2$

20) The bottom of a boat is 2y metres below the surface of the sea. A diver is swimming 5y metres below the bottom of the boat. The depth of the sea (from the surface to the sea-bed) is 16 metres. How far, in terms of y, is the diver above the sea-bed?

21) Make j the subject of the formula $k = 17 - {}^{4+j}\!/_{5}$

22) What is the volume of a fish tank in the shape of a cuboid 5f centimetres long, 4f centimetres wide and f centimetres high?

23) Simplify $\dfrac{5c}{3de} \div \dfrac{cd}{4e} \times \dfrac{2d}{5}$

24) The owner of a castle charged 80 pence admission for each adult and 45 pence for each child. Write a formula, beginning M =, to show the amount of money M, in pence, the owner received when A adults and C children visited his castle.

25) Simplify (i) $y \times y \times y \times y \times y \times y \times y$
(ii) $w + w + w + w + w + w$

26) Kevin thought of a number. He multiplied it by 3 and then subtracted 100. The result was $\frac{2}{9}$ of the number he first thought of. What was the number?

27) Find the value of t in the formula $t = \frac{1}{4}b^2c - 3cd$ when $b = 6$, $c = \frac{2}{3}$ and $d = -1$.

28) (i) Divide $3FG$ by $12F^3G^2$
(ii) Multiply $2c^2d^2t$ by $4c^3dt$

29) W is a whole number.
By solving the inequality $2(W + 10) - 5W < W - 11$,
find the least possible value that W can have.

30) Find the product of $-\frac{2}{3}$, $-\frac{4}{5}$ and $-\frac{5}{8}$ expressed in its simplest form.

31) Solve for c $\dfrac{2c + 7}{2} = c + \dfrac{c + 4}{3}$

32) Simplify (i) $5 - 11 + 3 - 1 + 7$
(ii) $9 - 2mp + 9mp - 6$

33) What is the value of $z(7 + z) - 3z^2$ when $z = 4$?

34) Find (i) the perimeter, and (ii) the area of a rectangular garden $(5t - 2)$ metres long and 3t metres wide.

35) (i) What are the next three consecutive numbers above $(x - 8)$?
(ii) If $x = 22$, what is the sum of the next three consecutive numbers above $(x - 8)$?

36) Simplify $\dfrac{5x}{4} + \dfrac{2x}{3} - \dfrac{x}{6}$

37) (i) Subtract $6 - 2y$ from $y - 2$.
(ii) To what must $4y^2 - yz$ be added to make $5yz + 2y^2$?

38) Multiply out and simplify $7(2q - h) - 4(2h + 3q)$

39) At Joe's snack bar, a mug of tea costs 9 pence and a mug of coffee costs 13 pence.

(i) Write a formula for the total cost A of t mugs of tea and c mugs of coffee.

(ii) A party of people bought mugs of tea and coffee at Joe's bar. They bought 12 mugs of coffee, and the total cost for their drinks was £2.82. By substituting in the formula (in PENCE), or any other way, find how many mugs of tea they bought.

40) Simplify (i) $\dfrac{12jk - 8kn}{4k}$

(ii) $\dfrac{4}{c} + \dfrac{2}{3c}$

41) Make q the subject of the formula $pr + 13q = 90$

42) Calculate the value of Q in the equation

$$3.7Q - 13.2 = 1.5Q$$

43) A bookseller received 3 boxes each containing $(v + 4)$ books and 2 boxes each containing $(2v - 1)$ books.

(i) How many books, in terms of v, did she receive?

(ii) She received 192 books altogether. Make an equation and solve for v.

44) (i) Find the sum of 6mn, 3np, 5mn and np.

(ii) Find the product of 5AB, 3AB and AB.

45) If $a = \frac{4}{5}$, $b = \frac{1}{2}$, $c = -5$, find the value of $4ab^2 + 3b + abc$

46) Multiply $8L^2M$ by $3M^2N$ and divide the result by $6LN$.

47) Simplify $2k(5 + k) - k(3k - 2) - 5k^2$ and factorise the result as fully as possible.

48) In a class of 23, G were girls.

(i) How many boys were there in the class?

(ii) One day, 2 of the boys were absent. How many boys were present?

49) Solve the inequality $\dfrac{2x-5}{6} + \dfrac{x+1}{2} \geqslant 8$

50) An electricity board charges each customer 1350 pence and then 7 pence for each unit of electricity the customer uses.

(i) Write a formula showing the total cost C if the customer uses u units of electricity.

(ii) A customer uses 248 units of electricity. How much is his total electricity bill? Give your answer in £.